WORLD OF READING

WORKBOOK

TEACHER EDITION

◆ ON THE ◆ HORIZON

P. DAVID PEARSON   DALE D. JOHNSON

THEODORE CLYMER   ROSELMINA INDRISANO   RICHARD L. VENEZKY

JAMES F. BAUMANN   ELFRIEDA HIEBERT   MARIAN TOTH

Consulting Authors

CARL GRANT   JEANNE PARATORE

SILVER BURDETT & GINN

NEEDHAM, MA · MORRISTOWN, NJ
ATLANTA, GA · CINCINNATI, OH · DALLAS, TX
MENLO PARK, CA · DEERFIELD, IL

Acknowledgments

Grateful acknowledgment is made to the following publishers, authors, and agents for their permission to reprint copyrighted material. Any adaptations are noted in the individual acknowledgments and are made with the full knowledge and approval of the authors or their representatives. Every effort has been made to locate all copyright proprietors; any errors or omissions in copyright notice are inadvertent and will be corrected in future printings as they are discovered.

Pages 125 and 138: Dictionary pronunciation key adapted from *Webster's New World Dictionary*, Basic School Edition, David B. Guralnik, Editor-in-Chief. Copyright © 1983 and 1979 by Simon & Schuster, Inc. Used by permission of the publisher.

Illustration Credits

Donna Ayers, pp. 93, 121; Yvette Banek, pp. 36, 37, 46, 106; Karen Barbour, pp. 97–99; Heidi Chang, p. 11; Olivia Cole, pp. 47, 62, 68, 105; Don Dyen, pp. 81–84; Len Ebert, pp. 18–21, 35, 63, 79, 96, 103; Marlene Ekman, pp. 8, 86; Ted Enik, p. 107; Debra Finn, pp. 87, 93; Simon Galkin, pp. 15, 16, 51, 89; Tom La Padula, pp. 67, 85; Glenna Lang, p. 14, 44; Yee Chea Lin, pp. 6, 17, 27, 49, 65, 70, 78, 88, 92, 114, 120; Morissa Lipstein, pp. 9, 10, 12, 104; Richard Loehle, pp. 69, 71, 118; Ben Mahan, pp. 26, 28, 48; Sal Murdocca, pp. 124, 132; James Needham, p. 59; Louis Pappas, pp. 50, 100, 125, 129–131, 133, 135–137; Jan Pyk, pp. 7, 13, 32, 34, 53–55, 60, 80, 91, 101, 102, 119, 128, 134; Steve Schindler, p. 25; Den Schofield, pp. 115, 117; Joel Snyder, pp. 24, 52, 58, 61; Sandra Speidel, pp. 120, 122, 123; Pat Stewart, pp. 64, 66; Joe Veno, pp. 29–31, 33, 90; Lane Yerkes, pp. 45, 116.

TABLE OF CONTENTS

TABLE OF CONTENTS

Interest Inventory

Each person is different from others in many special ways. What special things do you find in others? Answer the questions below and use the chart to discover books that you may find interesting.

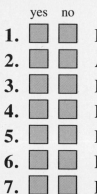

yes no

1. ☐ ☐ Do you ever want to be like someone else?
2. ☐ ☐ Are you interested in one special hobby?
3. ☐ ☐ Do you think it is hard to be different?
4. ☐ ☐ Do you sometimes like to be alone?
5. ☐ ☐ Do you like to imagine being able to do surprising things?
6. ☐ ☐ Do you like to do things that seem hard?
7. ☐ ☐ Do you enjoy funny stories about animals?

Now find the numbers for the questions you checked YES. Follow the column down. When you see a star, move across the row to find the book title. That's the book for you!

1	2	3	4	5	6	7	Title/Author
	★			★			*Liang and the Magic Paintbrush* by Demi
★				★			*The Luckiest One of All* by Bill Peet
		★			★		*Thinking Big* by Susan Kuklin
★			★			★	*The Lonely, Only Mouse* by Wendy Smith
★	★			★		★	*Angelina Ballerina* by Katharine Holabird
		★	★	★	★		*Johnny the Clockmaker* by Edward Ardizzone
		★			★		*Santiago* by Symeon Shimin

Personal Book List

NAME _____

Title _____

Author _____

Title _____

Author _____

Title _____

Author _____

Title _____

Author _____

Context Clues

> **REMEMBER:** The words and sentences around an unknown word can help you figure out the meaning of that unknown word.

A. Read each quote from "The Case of the Blond Wig." Write the word or words from the box that mean the same as the underlined word.

delayed	directed	last races	tied
detective work	excuse	removed	

1. "Idaville's war on crime was <u>masterminded</u> by their only child, ten-year-old Encyclopedia . . . ." _____ directed _____

2. "Chief Brown hated keeping his son's <u>sleuthing</u> undercover."
_____ detective work _____

3. "Chief Brown smiled and <u>withdrew</u> a small notebook from his breast pocket." _____ removed _____

4. "Isn't *Defiance* one of the sailboats in the Commodore's Cup <u>finals</u>?" Mrs. Brown inquired. _____ last races _____

5. "*Childhood II* might have beaten *Defiance* and <u>squared</u> the series at one victory apiece." _____ tied _____

6. "So the second race had to be <u>postponed</u> until tomorrow."
_____ delayed _____

7. "[The Cushing brothers] don't have an <u>alibi</u> for seven o'clock . . . . They insisted they were eating breakfast."
_____ excuse _____

B. The *Defiance* was a fast boat in rough seas. On separate paper, explain why *Defiance* is a good name for the Day's sailboat. See Teacher Notes.

NAME _____

Reality/Fantasy

> **REMEMBER:** A **realistic** story tells about things that could really happen. A **fantasy** tells about things that could not happen in real life.

A. Read each sentence. Write whether it describes *reality* or *fantasy*.

1. Abraham Lincoln often read books by the light of a fire.

   _____reality_____

2. Paul Bunyan roped the moon and pulled it down so he could read his book at night. _____fantasy_____

3. My grandfather had to walk three miles to school when he was a young boy. _____reality_____

4. John Lightfoot covered a mile with every step. _____fantasy_____

5. Mary didn't finish her homework because she was visiting with friends from outer space. _____fantasy_____

6. Fred's cousin is a famous football player who has won many awards over the years. _____reality_____

7. One winter when the Black River froze, I walked across it to the other side, where my friend lived. _____reality_____

8. Hannah runs as fast as birds can fly because she has wings on her heels. _____fantasy_____

B. Imagine that you found a magical blue rock in the street near your house. On separate paper, write a fantasy about what you did with the rock. See Teacher Notes.

Using New Words

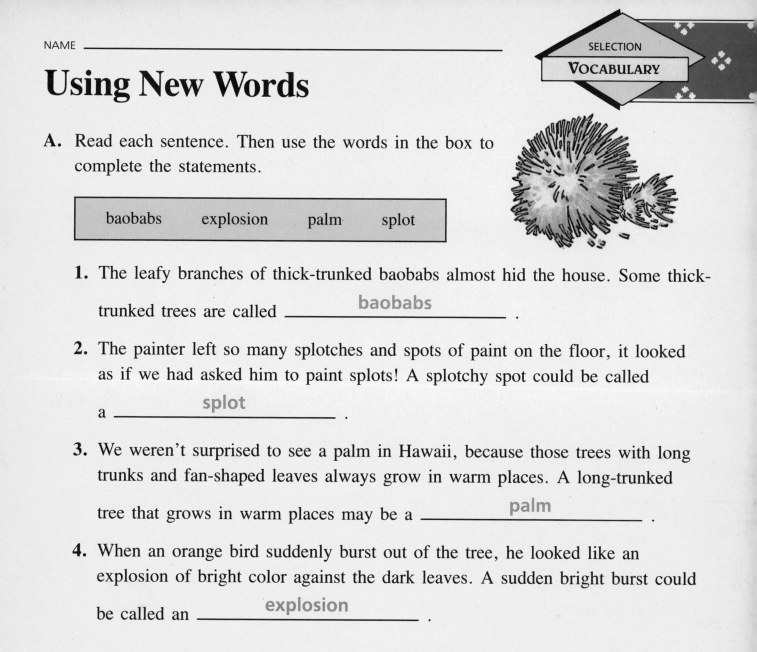

A. Read each sentence. Then use the words in the box to complete the statements.

baobabs	explosion	palm	splot

1. The leafy branches of thick-trunked baobabs almost hid the house. Some thick-trunked trees are called _____baobabs_____ .

2. The painter left so many splotches and spots of paint on the floor, it looked as if we had asked him to paint splots! A splotchy spot could be called a _____splot_____ .

3. We weren't surprised to see a palm in Hawaii, because those trees with long trunks and fan-shaped leaves always grow in warm places. A long-trunked tree that grows in warm places may be a _____palm_____ .

4. When an orange bird suddenly burst out of the tree, he looked like an explosion of bright color against the dark leaves. A sudden bright burst could be called an _____explosion_____ .

B. Write the three words from the box in Part A that match the headings below.

Words That Name Trees

_____palm_____

_____baobabs_____

A Word Made From Two Other Words

_____splot_____

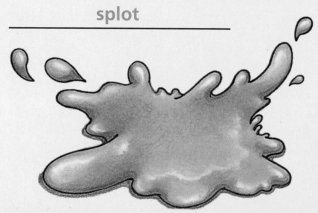

C. On separate paper, make a list of words like *splot* by combining two other words. (You can make up some of your own.) See Teacher Notes.

The Big Orange SPLOT

A. Complete the summary of the story "The Big Orange Splot."
Accept reasonable variations.

This story is about a man named _____ Mr. Plumbean _____

and his neighbors. They lived on a street where all the houses

_____ looked the same _____ .

Their neat street became not so neat when a sea gull

_____ dropped orange paint on Mr. Plumbean's house _____ .

This upset Mr. Plumbean's neighbors. They asked Mr. Plumbean to

_____ repaint his house _____ .

Mr. Plumbean painted his house with many colors of paint. His

house looked like a _____ rainbow, a jungle, an explosion _____ .

Next he built a tower. Then he put green things in his yard. When he

was finished, Mr. Plumbean said his house was him, where he liked to

be, and it looked _____ like his dreams _____ .

The neighbors said Mr. Plumbean's house had to be the same as

theirs so they could have _____ a neat street _____ . They sent a

man to talk to Mr. Plumbean. The next day the man changed his house

to look like _____ a ship _____ . The man said that his house was him,

where he liked to be, and it looked _____ like his dreams _____ .

One by one all the neighbors came to see Mr. Plumbean. The very

next day the person would change his house. Strangers would tell the

people that _____ their street wasn't neat _____ .

But the people would answer, "Our street is us and we are it. Our street

is where we like to be, and it looks like all our dreams."

B. On separate paper, write three sentences that tell how your one-
of-a-kind dream house would look. See Teacher Notes.

Homographs

> **REMEMBER: Homographs** are words that have the same spelling but different meanings and pronunciations. Use context to decide the correct meaning and pronunciation of a homograph.

A. Read each pair of sentences and meanings. Write the meaning that matches each underlined homograph.

1. Did Mr. Plumbean <u>lead</u> people to their dreams? ___b. show the way___

   The pipe is made of <u>lead</u>. ___a. soft metal___
   a. soft metal   b. show the way

2. Mr. Plumbean turned his yard into a jungle instead of a <u>desert</u>.
   ___a. place where few plants grow___

   The sailors had to <u>desert</u> the ship at the last minute. ___b. leave___
   a. place where few plants grow   b. leave

3. At <u>present</u> the class is studying homographs. ___b. now___

   The teacher will <u>present</u> prizes to the winners. ___a. give___
   a. give   b. now

4. The <u>wind</u> blew the trees in Mr. Plumbean's garden. ___a. moving air___

   I saw the dog <u>wind</u> the rope around the pole. ___b. turn many times___
   a. moving air   b. turn many times

B. On separate paper, write two sentences of your own for one pair of homographs in Part A. See Teacher Notes.

NAME _____

Context Clues

> **REMEMBER:** The words and sentences around an unknown word can help you figure out the meaning of that unknown word.

A. Read each pair of sentences. Look for clues to the meanings of the underlined words. Then write the meanings on the lines to complete the sentences.

1. Mr. Plumbean liked all shades of red, but <u>crimson</u> and <u>scarlet</u> were two of his favorites.

   Crimson and scarlet are _____ shades of red _____ .

2. He painted not only the frames of his windows and shutters, but also the <u>mullions</u> and <u>sills</u> and even several glass <u>panes</u>!

   Mullions, sills, and panes are parts of _____ windows _____ .

3. He planted palms and <u>banyans</u> alongside the pines and maples in his yard.

   Banyans are probably a kind of _____ tree _____ .

4. In addition to his sea gull, Mr. Plumbean gathered <u>terns</u>, <u>plovers</u>, and even a <u>flamingo</u> because he liked their colorful wings.

   Terns, plovers, and flamingos are _____ birds _____ .

5. Mr. Plumbean's neighbor dreamed of a ship, and the next day he used lumber, rope, and paint to change his house into a <u>schooner</u>.

   A schooner is a kind of _____ ship _____ .

6. After the first neighbor changed his house, then all the neighbors <u>transformed</u> their houses.

   Transformed means _____ changed _____ .

B. On separate paper, write two sentences of your own in which context clues show the meanings of *scarlet* and *flamingo*. **See Teacher Notes.**

Synonyms/Antonyms

> **REMEMBER: Synonyms** are words that mean about the same thing. *Big* and *large* are synonyms. **Antonyms** are words that have opposite meanings. *Stop* and *go* are antonyms. *Tall* and *short* are also antonyms.

A. Underline the synonyms in each pair of sentences. Then write them.

1. **a.** Mr. Plumbean looked at the <u>big</u> orange splot. _____ big

   b. Mr. Plumbean looked at the <u>large</u> orange splot. _____ large

2. **a.** Neighbors got tired of <u>seeing</u> the splot. _____ seeing

   b. Neighbors got tired of <u>viewing</u> the splot. _____ viewing

3. **a.** Mr. Plumbean painted <u>different</u> colors by the splot. _____ different

   b. Mr. Plumbean painted <u>various</u> colors by the splot. _____ various

B. Underline the antonyms in each pair of sentences. Then write them.

4. People <u>came</u> out of their houses to look at Mr. Plumbean's house. Then they <u>went</u> into their own houses and wondered. _____ went   came

5. Some people <u>shouted</u> at Mr. Plumbean. Other people <u>whispered</u> that he had lost his marbles. _____ whispered   shouted

6. People talked to Mr. Plumbean <u>late</u> at night. <u>Early</u> the next day, they started changing their houses. _____ early   late

C. On separate paper, write five words that tell about how your dream house would look. Then write a synonym for one word and an antonym for another. See Teacher Notes.

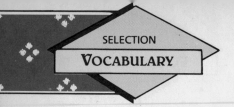

Using New Words

A. Find the answers to the riddles. Write the story word that means almost the same thing as the underlined word or words.

conservatory	jasmine	lanes	lupines	rose-colored

1. We are beautiful in purple, rose, and blue.

   We are <u>garden flowers</u>. We are _____lupines_____ .

2. We are <u>narrow paths</u> between walls or buildings.

   We are _____lanes_____ .

3. I smell very sweet. I am a <u>tropical plant</u>.

   I am a _____jasmine_____ .

4. Things that are my color are <u>pinkish</u>.

   I am _____rose-colored_____ .

5. I am a <u>room made of glass</u> where plants grow.

   I am a _____conservatory_____ .

B. Write the story words that belong in each group.

6. Word that names types of roads

   _____lanes_____

7. Words that name plants and flowers

   _____lupines_____

   _____jasmine_____

8. Word that tells about color

   _____rose-colored_____

C. On separate paper, write a riddle using as many story words as you can. See Teacher Notes.

Miss Rumphius

A. Complete the summary of the story "Miss Rumphius."
Accept reasonable variations.

This story is about a woman named _____ Miss Rumphius _____ .

The story takes place in a town near _____ the sea _____ .

As a little girl, Miss Rumphius was called Alice. Her grandfather told Alice about faraway places. Alice told him that when she grew up, she would live near the sea and visit faraway places. Her grandfather also told her to make the world _____ more beautiful _____ .

When Alice grew up, she moved to a city and worked _____ _____ in a library _____ . She would often go to the conservatory. It reminded her of a tropical isle. One day she went to _____ a real tropical island _____ . She also traveled to mountains, jungles, and deserts. When she hurt her back one day, she decided it was time to _____ go to a place by the sea _____ .

There was still one thing she hadn't done. She had to do something to _____ make the world more beautiful _____ . She planted a small garden and thought.

The next summer Miss Rumphius looked at her garden and the lupines she had planted. She found that the _____ wind and birds _____ had brought seeds from her garden to new places. That gave her the idea to _____ plant lupines everywhere _____ . That is how Miss Rumphius became known as _____ the Lupine Lady _____ and how she made the world more beautiful.

B. Imagine what you could do to make your neighborhood more beautiful. On separate paper, write a story telling what you would do. See Teacher Notes.

VOCABULARY

Synonyms/Antonyms

> **REMEMBER: Synonyms** are words that have similar meanings. *Big* and *large* are synonyms. **Antonyms** are words that have opposite or nearly opposite meanings. *Stop* and *go* are antonyms. *Tall* and *short* are also antonyms.

A. Write a synonym for each underlined word.

| distant   pretty   silly   tiny |

1. ___tiny___ The Lupine Lady lived in a <u>small</u> house.

2. ___distant___ Her grandfather had told her of <u>faraway</u> places.

3. ___pretty___ Sometimes she picked up <u>beautiful</u> shells on beaches.

4. ___silly___ Miss Rumphius said she had been <u>foolish</u> to hurt herself getting off a camel.

B. Write an antonym of your own for each underlined word. **Responses may vary.**

5. ___hated___ Like her grandfather, Miss Rumphius <u>loved</u> to travel.

6. ___few___ She made <u>many</u> friends on her trips to faraway places.

7. ___ugly___ One friend gave her a <u>lovely</u> present so she would remember him.

8. ___never___ Miss Rumphius <u>always</u> thought of him fondly.

C. Think of three pairs of antonyms. On separate paper, use each of your antonyms in a sentence. See Teacher Notes.

Making an Alike-and-Different Chart

> **REMEMBER:** You can understand stories better by thinking about how a story character is the same as or different from someone you know.

A. In the story "Miss Rumphius," Alice Rumphius greatly admired her grandfather. Read about him in the alike-and-different chart. Then think about a person you admire. Write something about that person in the chart next to each description of Alice's grandfather. Tell how the person is like or different from him.

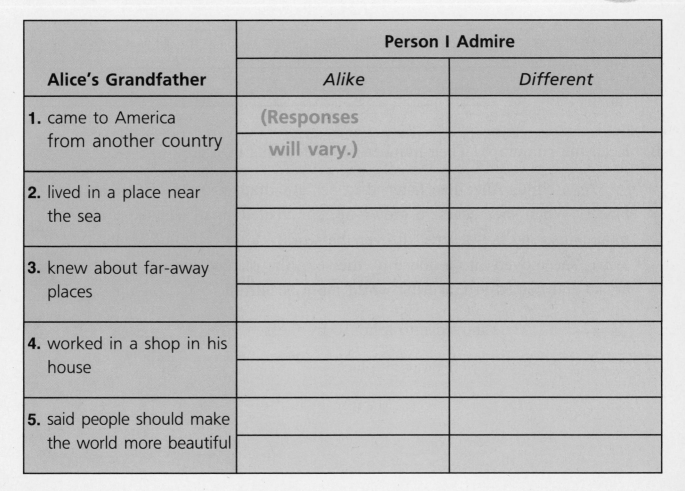

Alice's Grandfather	Person I Admire	
	Alike	*Different*
1. came to America from another country	(Responses will vary.)	
2. lived in a place near the sea		
3. knew about far-away places		
4. worked in a shop in his house		
5. said people should make the world more beautiful		

B. On a separate paper, write a sentence telling how you are like Alice when she was young. See Teacher Notes.

NAME _____

Sequence

> **REMEMBER: Sequence** is the order in which things happen in a story. Look for signal words and story clues to figure out the sequence.

A. Write the events in this paragraph in the correct order.

Miss Rumphius woke up when the alarm went off at 7:00 A.M. as she did every morning. Then she reached over and turned off the alarm. This morning, however, she stayed in bed for quite a while and thought about the things that had happened the day before. It was 7:35 A.M. before Miss Rumphius finally sat up, stretched, and got out of bed.

At 7:00 A.M. _Miss Rumphius woke up._

Then _she turned off the alarm._

Finally _she got up._

B. Read the paragraph. Then number the statements in order.

As a child, Alice had listened to her grandfather's talk of distant places. When she became a grown-up, she visited small islands, giant mountains, and hot deserts all over the world. After traveling so far away, she moved into a house by the sea. She planted lupines near her house and helped to make the world more beautiful.

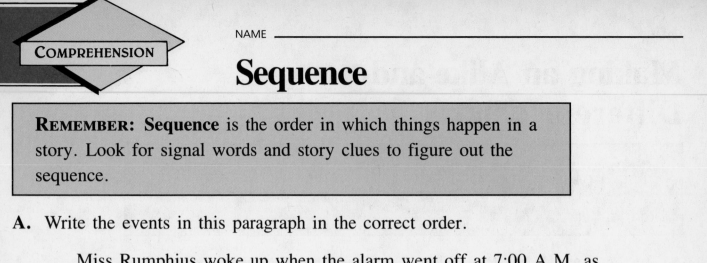

____3____ **a.** Alice moved into a house by the sea.

____2____ **b.** She visited faraway places.

____4____ **c.** She made the world more beautiful.

____1____ **d.** Alice learned about the world from her grandfather.

C. On separate paper, write about something you did last week. Use signal words like *after* and *then*. See Teacher Notes.

Using New Words

A. Use the words from the box to complete the sentences.

composer	concert	conductor	extraordinary
orchestra	violin	violinist	

1. A young _____ composer _____ has written a new piece of music.

2. She wants the whole _____ orchestra _____ to play it.

3. She thinks we should invite our parents to a _____ concert _____ .

4. All of the musicians will be led by a _____ conductor _____ .

5. A solo will be played on the _____ violin _____ by a _____ violinist _____ .

6. We hope our parents will think our concert is _____ extraordinary _____ .

B. Write words from the box to finish the sentences.

7. A group of musicians forms an _____ orchestra _____ .

8. A musical performance is a _____ concert _____ .

9. A musical instrument is a _____ violin _____ .

10. Something that is out of the ordinary is _____ extraordinary _____ .

C. Imagine you are a conductor. On separate paper, write a story about the kind of concert you would conduct. Use as many story words as you can. See Teacher Notes.

NAME

Mi Dori

A. Complete the summary of "Mi Dori."

Accept reasonable variations.

This selection is about a young violinist named

<u>Mi Dori</u> . It begins on a hot, summer night in

<u>Tanglewood, Massachusetts</u> .

Mi Dori was playing her solo when, suddenly, one of the

<u>strings</u> on her violin <u>broke</u> . Quickly she

turned to another violinist and <u>borrowed his violin</u> .

A minute later a string on that violin broke, too. She borrowed still

another violin. Mi Dori continued to play and didn't make any mistakes.

At the end, everyone cheered young Mi Dori's performance.

The next day <u>newspapers/reporters</u>

all over the United States told about her amazing performance. Both

violins Mi Dori had borrowed were <u>bigger</u> than her

own. Hers was smaller because Mi Dori was small and only fourteen

years old. But on the bigger violins, she had not missed a note.

Mi Dori began playing violin when she was four in her own country,

<u>Japan</u> . She and her mother had moved to the United States

so she could study with Dorothy DeLay, a famous American violin

teacher.

Mi Dori has an extraordinary talent. She has played many concerts,

including a Christmas show at the <u>White House</u> .

Everywhere she plays, audiences praise her because they know

they are listening to one of the best <u>violinists</u>

of any age.

B. On separate paper, write a short letter to the student who may
get your reading book next year. Tell what you liked or didn't
like about "Mi Dori." See Teacher Notes.

Sequence

> **REMEMBER: Sequence** is the order in which things happen in a story. Look for signal words and story clues to figure out the sequence.

A. Read the paragraph about Mi Dori. Then number the events in the order they happened.

     At the start of the concert everything went fine for Mi Dori. She played beautifully, and the audience loved her music. Then suddenly a string broke on her violin. Mi Dori quickly borrowed a violin. Even though this violin was much larger than her own, she continued playing beautifully. Then, unbelievably, a string broke on the borrowed violin. Mi Dori had to borrow another one. Even so, she went on playing beautifully!

___3___ **a.** Then a second string broke!

___1___ **b.** Mi Dori began her solo.

___4___ **c.** At last she completed her solo with a third violin.

___2___ **d.** Her violin string broke, and she had to borrow an instrument.

B. These events are out of order. Number them so they are in the correct order.

___2___ **a.** Next Mi Dori's mother sent her a tape of Mi Dori playing the violin.

___1___ **b.** First Mi Dori's mother heard that the famous American violinist Ms. DeLay was visiting Japan.

___3___ **c.** At last Mi Dori and her mother moved to the United States so Mi Dori could study with Ms. DeLay.

C. On separate paper, write about three steps you would take to learn to play an instrument. **See Teacher Notes.**

Checkpoint

Read the paragraphs. Then fill in the circle beside the correct answer.

Maria woke up. She was cold. The fire she had made the night before was out. She dressed herself under the covers where it was warm. Then she got up. There were no logs in the wood box by the stove, so she would have to get some from outside.

First she put on her heavy coat and hat. When she was warmly dressed, she opened the door and went outside. The wood she had cut yesterday was piled near the door. Maria picked up as much as she could hold and carried it into the house. She put some pieces into the stove before she went out to get more. Finally, when she had finished carrying in the wood, she knelt by the stove and started a new fire.

Once the fire was warm and crackling, she picked up a pail and went outside again. She filled the pail with water. Before she brought the water into the house, she fed the three chickens and got the eggs. When she was back in the house, she thought about all her chores. Taking care of the cabin while her parents were away was not an easy job, but she was proud to be able to do it just the same.

sequence

1. Which event happened first?

   (a) Maria looked in the wood box.

   (b) The fire went out.

   (c) Maria got dressed.

   (d) Maria got out of bed.

sequence

2. Which sentence from the story helped you choose your answer?

   (a) Maria woke up.

   (b) She was cold.

   (c) The fire she had made the night before was out.

   (d) Then she got up.

sequence

3. What did Maria do before she went outside?

a) She started a fire.

b) She put wood in the stove.

c) She put on her coat and hat.

d) She picked up an armful of wood.

sequence

4. Which word from the story helped you choose your answer?

a) first

b) before

c) finally

d) once

sequence

5. What was the last thing Maria did before she went outside with her pail?

a) She fed the chickens.

b) She went out to get more wood.

c) She started a new fire.

d) She got dressed.

sequence

6. Which word from the story helped you choose your answer?

a) first

b) before

c) finally

d) once

sequence

7. What did Maria do before she brought water into the house?

a) She went to school.

b) She ate breakfast.

c) She thought about her chores.

d) She fed the chickens.

sequence

8. Which words from the story helped you choose your answer?

a) She filled the pail with water.

b) Before she brought water into the house . . .

c) When she was back in the house . . .

d) She thought about her chores.

COMPREHENSION

Cause/Effect

> **REMEMBER:** Use signal words, story clues, and what you already know to figure out which events caused other events to happen.

A. Read the paragraph. Fill in the causes and effects.

It was a very hot night so the orchestra members took off their jackets and left them backstage. They began to play. Because she was small, Mi Dori was playing a small violin. A string broke on her violin, and she had to borrow an instrument from the violinist behind her. Then a string broke on that violin, and she had to borrow still another violin! Both borrowed violins seemed too big for Mi Dori. One violinist wanted to fix Mi Dori's violin, but his extra strings were in his jacket backstage. Mi Dori continued playing on the large violin. She played so well that the audience cheered.

1. Cause: It was a very hot night.

   Effect: The musicians left their jackets backstage.

2. Cause: Mi Dori's violin string broke.

   Effect: Mi Dori had to borrow two different violins.

3. Cause: One violinist's extra strings were backstage.

   Effect: He was unable to fix Mi Dori's violin.

4. Cause: Mi Dori played very well even though the violin was large.

   Effect: The audience cheered.

B. Imagine that you break the point of your only pencil in the middle of a test. On separate paper, describe three effects this might cause. See Teacher Notes.

Using New Words

A. Complete each sentence with the correct story word. Use each word once.

animal groomer	assigned	calculator	word processor
librarian	nickname	unusual	

1. Some people have a special name or __nickname__ they are known by.

2. These special names are often funny or __unusual__ .

3. For example, a __librarian__ might be called ''Books'' by his friends.

4. A person who works with a __calculator__ all day might be known as ''Numbers.''

5. Someone who is a whiz on a __word processor__ might be called ''The Writer'' at work.

6. I knew an __animal groomer__ who was called ''The Beast Comber'' because she brushed and combed animals' coats.

7. It might be fun to be __assigned__ the job of thinking up a special name for everyone in your family.

B. Write the story words that belong in the following groups.

8. Things that can help you at school __calculator, word processor__

9. People with interesting jobs __animal groomer, librarian__

C. Think of two funny nicknames. On separate paper, use these two nicknames and two story words in a short paragraph. See Teacher Notes.

Ali Baba Bernstein

A. Complete the summary of the story "Ali Baba Bernstein."
Accept reasonable variations.

This story is about a boy named **David** Bernstein who

decided to change his name to **Ali Baba** . The story

takes place in **New York City** .

David Bernstein was eight years, five months, and seventeen days

old when he **decided to change his name** .

David's teacher assigned **a book report** with extra

credit for fat books. His mother guessed the fattest book must be the

Manhattan **telephone book** . David was

interested to find in it seventeen listings for people named David

Bernstein. The next day David began reading *The Arabian Nights*. The

book was good, and in it David found his new name.

David told everyone he wanted to be called _____

Ali Baba Bernstein . Then it came time to

plan his ninth birthday party. He wanted to invite **all the people**

in the phone book named David Bernstein .

On the evening of the party the living room filled with people

named **David Bernstein** . There was a

television director, a delicatessen owner, a mailman, an animal groomer,

a dentist, a teacher, and a writer. David told them why he had changed

his name. But one person said, "Just because we have the same name

doesn't make us **the same** ." Ali Baba had to agree.

They *were* all different.

B. Think of a nickname you would like to be called. On a separate
paper, write three sentences telling why you think the nickname
suits you. **See Teacher Notes.**

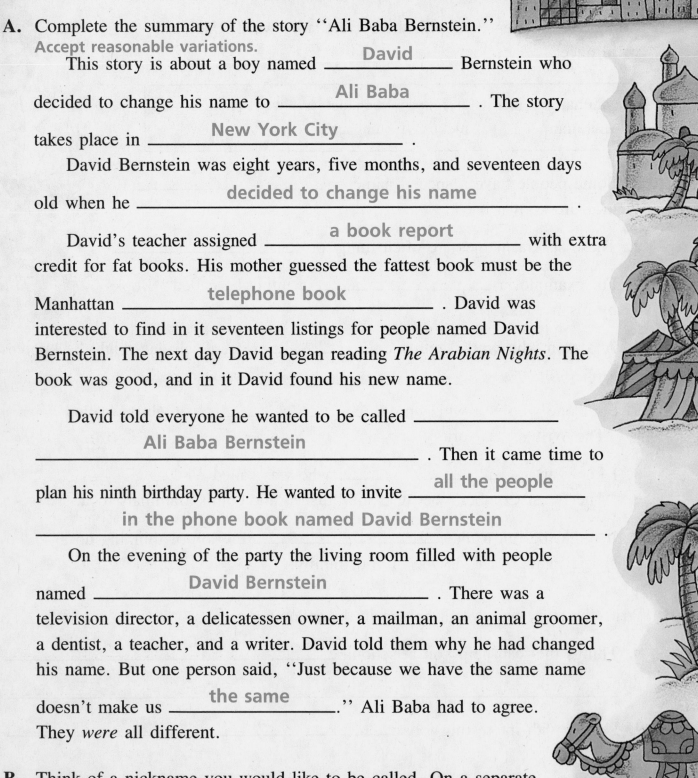

Telephone Directory

> **REMEMBER:** Use the white pages to find telephone numbers of specific people or businesses. Use the yellow pages to identify businesses that sell products or services you want or need.

A. Write each name the way it would be listed in the white pages.

1. Ali Baba Bernstein _____ Bernstein, Ali Baba _____

2. Joan S. Booxbaum _____ Booxbaum, Joan S. _____

3. Leroy's Computer Factory _____ Leroy's Computer Factory _____

4. Darlene P. Hunt _____ Hunt, Darlene P. _____

B. Read the sample from the yellow pages. Then answer the questions.

MUSIC LESSONS

BAKER'S MUSIC VILLAGE
    120 Main Street 555–0001
CARREN'S MUSIC SCHOOL
    33 River Road 555–0690
DAN'S VIOLIN SCHOOL
    801 East Broadway 555–2127
GUITAR FOR YOU
    2400 First Avenue 555–9806

5. Where might you call for violin lessons? _____ Dan's Violin School _____

6. What is the telephone number of Carren's Music School? _____ 555–0690 _____

7. What is the address of Guitar for You? _____ 2400 First Avenue _____

C. On separate paper, make your own phone book by writing your friends' names in alphabetical order next to their addresses and phone numbers. See Teacher Notes.

Sequence

NAME

> **REMEMBER: Sequence** is the order in which things happen in a story. Look for signal words and story clues to figure out the sequence.

A. Read the paragraph. Then number the statements in order.

   One day David's teacher promised extra credit for a report on a fat book. David wanted to read the longest book, so he decided to report on the New York phone book. After he had read all the A pages, however, he decided that the phone book was not interesting. He began to read *The Arabian Nights* instead. It was shorter than the phone book but much more fun.

___3___ **a.** He read the A pages.

___1___ **b.** David's teacher assigned a report.

___5___ **c.** He began to read *The Arabian Nights*.

___4___ **d.** He decided the phone book was long but too dull.

___2___ **e.** David chose the phone book for his report.

B. The following events are out of order. Number them correctly.

___3___ **a.** Then he made invitations on his father's word processor.

___4___ **b.** At last David met several people with his name at the party.

___1___ **c.** First David chose the name Ali Baba from *The Arabian Nights*.

___2___ **d.** Next he decided to invite all the David Bernsteins to his party.

C. Imagine you can do anything you want to on your birthday. On separate paper, describe what you would do. Use signal words to show the order of events. **See Teacher Notes.**

Main Idea/Details

REMEMBER: A **main idea** tells the topic of the paragraph and what the paragraph says about the topic.

A. Read the paragraphs. Write an answer to each question.

1. My ninth birthday party was the best I ever had. I invited new and old friends. I received many great gifts, including a jigsaw puzzle and some books. Best of all, we played some fun games.

a. Which sentence tells the main idea? _My ninth birthday party was the_ _best I ever had._

b. Which sentences tell details about the birthday party? _I invited new and_ _old friends. I received many great gifts, including a jigsaw puzzle_ _and some books. Best of all, we played some fun games._

2. For my birthday party, my friends and I went on a special train ride. First we went to the zoo. Inside we walked to the special train. The train took us all around the zoo. From the train cars, we saw many animals.

a. Which sentence tells the main idea? _For my birthday party,_ _my friends and I went on a special train ride._

b. Which sentences tell details about the party? _First we went to the zoo._ _Inside we walked to a special train. The train took us all_ _around the zoo. From the train cars, we saw many animals._

B. On separate paper, write a paragraph about a day you especially enjoyed. Begin with the main idea. Then write two sentences with details about the day. See Teacher Notes.

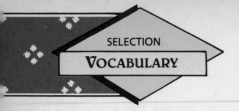

Using New Words

A. Use the words in the box to complete the sentences.

arches	blood vessels	characteristics	identify
loops	pattern	pupil	retina

1. Strength, balance, grace, and good timing are

_____characteristics_____ of a good dancer.

2. You can sometimes _____identify_____ a very strong person

by looking for well-developed muscles.

3. An artistic person may be able to see an arrangement, or a

_____pattern_____ , where others see only odd

shapes or lines.

4. An athlete is likely to have healthy _____blood vessels_____

because exercise helps your blood flow smoothly and steadily.

B. Write four words from the box under the headings.

5. Parts of an Eye

_____pupil_____

_____retina_____

6. Parts of Fingerprints

_____arches_____

_____loops_____

C. On separate paper, write three sentences, each about a different
person. Use at least one word from the box in each sentence.
See Teacher Notes.

No Two People Are the Same

A. Complete the summary of "No Two People Are the Same."
Accept reasonable variations.

This selection gives information about how your way of speaking,

your fingerprints, and even your eyes are _____ different _____

from anyone else's. It tells how you are one of a kind.

Your _____ fingerprints _____ have patterns of circles,

arches, and loops. If you put _____ ink _____ on your fingertips and

roll them on paper, you can see the pattern. Today

_____ computers _____ "read" fingerprints just like food

packages are "read" by computers at the supermarket.

Your eyes are also one of a kind. In the center is a dark spot called

the _____ pupil _____ . Light passes through it to the back part of your

eye, which is called the retina. The blood vessels in that retina make a

pattern that is yours alone.

Your voice is also one of a kind. When you speak, _____ air _____

travels from your lungs through your throat into your _____

_____ voice box _____ and to your mouth and nose. All the places

inside have shapes different from anyone else's, making your voice

different from everyone else's. A machine called a sound spectrograph

can make a picture of your voice called a _____ voiceprint _____ .

This will not always identify you, however, because even your own

voice _____ changes _____ when you have a cold.

In the future, computers may be used in homes to identify people by

their fingers, their eyes, and their voices.

B. On separate paper, make a chart showing how you are different
in three ways from another person in your own family. See Teacher Notes.

NAME _____

Author's Purpose

> **REMEMBER:** As you read, ask yourself if an author is writing to entertain you or to inform you.

A. Read the paragraphs. To tell the author's purpose, write *to entertain* or *to inform* after each paragraph.

1.   Joe and his twin brother look the same. One day they went to the store to buy books. The salesperson who helped them exclaimed, "I can't tell which of you is which!"
    "Yes, you can," said Joe. "I'm the talkative one. I love to hear my own voice. I speak up all the time. I talk nonstop. I talk so much that my twin never says anything. Isn't that right, Tom?"
    Tom nodded.

Author's Purpose: _____ to entertain _____

2.   Scientists have learned that each person's ears are different. No two people have ears that are exactly the same size and shape. It is even possible to identify someone by the shape of his or her ears. But fingerprints are an easier method of identification.

Author's Purpose: _____ to inform _____

B. Write the words in the box under the correct heading.

| encyclopedia | poem |
| tale | textbook |

3. To Entertain

tale
_____
poem
_____

4. To Inform

textbook
_____
encyclopedia
_____

C. On separate paper, write two paragraphs, one to entertain and one to inform. See Teacher Notes.

Context Clues

> **REMEMBER:** The words and sentences around an unknown word can help you figure out the meaning of that unknown word.

A. Use clues in each sentence to find the meaning of the underlined word. Write the meaning on the line.

1. Fingerprints that are <u>visible</u> are ones that can be seen.

can be seen

2. Scientists use a <u>laser</u>, which is something that gives out a powerful beam of light, to find invisible fingerprints.

something that gives out a powerful beam of light

3. Fingerprints have a <u>pattern</u>, or special shapes, of circles, loops, and arches.

special shapes

4. Light enters your eye and hits the <u>retina</u>, the back part of the eye.

the back part of the eye

5. Light enters the eye through the <u>pupil</u>, the dark spot in the center of the eye.

the dark spot in the center of the eye

6. A <u>sound spectrograph</u>, a special machine that draws pictures of sound, can tell the difference between different people's voices.

a special machine that draws pictures of sound

B. On separate paper, write two sentences about yourself that tell why you are special. In one sentence tell about your thumbprint and in the other tell about your eyes. See Teacher Notes.

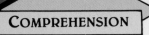
NAME _____

Sequence

REMEMBER: Sequence is the order in which things happen in a story. Look for signal words and story clues to figure out the sequence.

A. Read the sentences. Decide which event happened first and write it on the line.

1. After Maria looked into the scanner, a light studied her eye.

   Maria looked into the scanner.
   _____

2. The scanner read the pattern of blood vessels in Maria's eye. Then it could tell who she was.

   The scanner read the pattern of blood vessels in Maria's eye.
   _____

3. Before the black box opened, Maria placed her left thumb on the cover.

   Maria placed her left thumb on the cover.
   _____

4. Once the computer had been given information about Maria's fingers, it could identify her from her fingerprint patterns.

   The computer had been given information about Maria's fingers.
   _____

5. Scientists made a voiceprint of Joe's voice. The next morning his voiceprint was different because he had a cold.

   Scientists made a voiceprint of Joe's voice.
   _____

6. His swollen nose and throat changed his voice after his cold began.

   His cold began.
   _____

B. On separate paper, describe three early morning activities you do in order. Use signal words. **See Teacher Notes.**

Using New Words

A. Use a word from the box to complete each sentence.

awards	characters	cherishes	essay	experiences	novel

1. An author whose books have won many ___*awards*___ came to talk to our class last week.

2. She told us how she got the ideas for some of the things she wrote about in her newest ___*novel*___ .

3. To make the story interesting, she mixed real ___*experiences*___ with events that she made up.

4. Many of the experiences and memories she discussed are ones she still ___*cherishes*___ and will never forget.

5. We also discovered that some of the ___*characters*___ in her story are real people she has known.

6. When she left, our teacher asked us to write an ___*essay*___ about what it means to be an author.

B. Think of a book you have read and enjoyed. On separate paper, write a letter telling the author what you liked about the book. Use at least three words from the box in your letter. See Teacher Notes.

LEE BENNETT HOPKINS INTERVIEWS

Beverly Cleary

A. Complete the summary of "Lee Bennett Hopkins Interviews Beverly Cleary." Accept reasonable variations.

This selection is an interview with the author __Beverly Cleary__ . It tells about her life, how she writes books, and what she writes about.

Beverly Bunn Cleary grew up on a ___farm___ in Oregon. Young Beverly's mother told her stories. Beverly also loved to ___read___ . After college, Beverly Cleary became a children's ___librarian___ . Later, she moved to California with her husband. In their new house, she found some piles of ___typing paper___ in a drawer. Beverly Cleary decided it was time for her to ___write a book___ .

When she was a librarian, she heard some boys complain because the stories they read weren't about "children like us." That is why Mrs. Cleary likes to write about ___ordinary___ boys and girls.

People ask Mrs. Cleary about how she writes. She tells people she writes stories that she enjoys. "Writing is a pleasure. If I didn't enjoy writing, no one would enjoy reading my books."

Mrs. Cleary has received many ___awards___ for her books. The awards she cherishes most are ones from ___children___ . When Mrs. Cleary speaks about reading, she says, "When you read, good things happen. Your life becomes more ___interesting___ and so do you. So grab a book."

B. On separate paper, write a question you would like to ask Beverly Cleary. Then write the answer you think Beverly Cleary might give. See Teacher Notes.

Synonyms/Antonyms

> **REMEMBER: Synonyms** are words that mean about the same thing. *Big* and *large* are synonyms. **Antonyms** are words that have opposite or nearly opposite meanings. *Stop* and *go* are antonyms. *Tall* and *short* are also antonyms.

A. Read each pair of sentences. Underline the synonyms.

    1. a. Beverly Cleary became an <u>author</u> of children's books.
      b. Beverly Cleary became a <u>writer</u> of children's books.

    2. a. She has won many <u>awards</u> for her novels.
      b. She has won many <u>prizes</u> for her novels.

B. Read the sentences. Think of an antonym for each underlined word. Then write your antonym to finish the sentence.

    3. As a child, Beverly Cleary read about both <u>rich</u> children

    and _____poor_____ ones.

    4. She thought children's books were too <u>serious</u>, so she tried to make her

    stories lively and _____funny_____ .

C. Read the pairs of words. Write **A** on the blank if the words are antonyms. Write **S** if they are synonyms.

    5. sick } ___S___   **6.** good } ___A___
        ill   evil

    7. fat } ___A___   **8.** ocean } ___S___
        thin   sea

D. On separate paper, write two sentences about the kinds of stories you like to read. Use a pair of synonyms and a pair of antonyms in your sentences. **See Teacher Notes.**

Checkpoint

Read the paragraphs. Then fill in the circle beside the correct answer.

Danny was a snakesitter. He began his strange occupation by accident. One day he was trying to think of a way to make money. Then his friend Eddie came over. Eddie said his family was supposed to go on a trip. They couldn't leave until they found someone to take care of their pet snake. The people who took care of their dog detested snakes. They hated snakes so much they wouldn't even look at them. Eddie's family didn't know what to do. Eddie wondered if Danny would take care of the snake. Danny was excited. He was also dubious that his mother would let him take the job. But even though he didn't expect her to agree, he asked her anyway. She surprised him. She said it was all right.

After that first job, Danny made a sign to put in the pet shop. The sign said he would take care of snakes for a fair price. Because snakesitters were hard to find and usually cost a lot, Danny got a lot of jobs. Danny had found an unusual way to make money.

synonyms/antonyms

1. Choose the synonym for the underlined word <u>occupation</u>.

- (a) idea
- **(b) job**
- (c) life
- (d) day

context clues

2. Choose the sentence from the story that helped you understand the meaning of <u>occupation</u>.

- **(a) One day he was trying to think of a way to make money.**
- (b) Then his friend Eddie came over.
- (c) Eddie said his family was supposed to go on a trip.
- (d) Eddie's family didn't know what to do.

synonyms/antonyms

3. Choose the antonym for the underlined word <u>detested</u>.

- (a) hated
- (b) raised
- **(c) loved**
- (d) watched

context clues

4. Choose the sentence from the story that helped you understand the meaning of <u>detested</u>.

- (a) Eddie wondered if Danny would take care of the snake.
- (b) Eddie's family didn't know what to do.
- **(c) They hated snakes so much they wouldn't even look at them.**
- (d) Danny was excited.

synonyms/antonyms

5. Choose the synonym for the underlined word <u>dubious</u>.

- (a) sure
- (b) happy
- (c) excited
- **(d) doubtful**

context clues

6. Choose the sentence from the story that helped you understand the meaning of <u>dubious</u>.

- (a) Danny was excited.
- **(b) But even though he didn't expect her to agree, he asked her anyway.**
- (c) She surprised him.
- (d) She said it was all right.

Vocabulary Review

Fill in the circle beside the word that best fits in the sentence.

1. Because Dad wanted to plant a tropical tree, he planted a _____ .
   a) splot
   b) palm
   c) flake
   d) pitcher

2. For a short form of her name, we gave Elizabeth the _____ Liz.
   a) nickname
   b) calculator
   c) word processor
   d) novel

3. The person who cares for books in a library is called a _____ .
   a) violinist
   b) conductor
   c) librarian
   d) composer

4. All the people, or _____ , in the story were children.
   a) awards
   b) experiences
   c) lupines
   d) characters

5. The narrow paths between the buildings in the old part of Charleston, South Carolina, are called _____ .
   a) lanes
   b) lupines
   c) baobabs
   d) jasmine

6. The arrangement of lines, or the _____ , on your fingertips is what makes your fingerprints special.
   a) pattern
   b) pupil
   c) violin
   d) pockets

7. Alan saw an irregular-shaped _____ of paint on the floor.
   a) arches
   b) lanes
   c) splot
   d) essay

8. Evelyn has circle-like shapes, or _____ , as part of the pattern on her fingertips.

- (a) awards
- (b) loops
- (c) retina
- (d) lanes

9. The students who played musical instruments formed an _____ .

- (a) explosion
- (b) orchestra
- (c) essay
- (d) alphabet

10. Grandmother is very wise because she lived through many _____ during her life.

- (a) experiences
- (b) characters
- (c) loops
- (d) awards

11. The black part of the eye, or the _____ , is surrounded by the colored part.

- (a) pattern
- (b) essay
- (c) pupil
- (d) splot

12. To play the violin so well by the age of six was _____ .

- (a) extraordinary
- (b) discontented
- (c) boring
- (d) worthy

13. Mi Dori performed in a program of music, or a _____ , at Tanglewood.

- (a) orchestra
- (b) computer
- (c) concert
- (d) pattern

14. The author Beverly Cleary has received many prizes, or _____ , for her children's stories.

- (a) awards
- (b) experiences
- (c) arches
- (d) baobabs

15. The room that had glass walls and a glass roof, or the _____ , had many bird-of-paradise plants.

- (a) jasmine
- (b) composer
- (c) conservatory
- (d) explosion

Unit Wrap-Up

NAME _____

Read each question. Write your answer, using complete sentences.

1. What special talents make Beverly Cleary and Mi Dori different from other people? **Possible response: Beverly Cleary has a talent for writing interesting books for children. Mi Dori has a talent for playing the violin.**

2. Think about the story "Ali Baba Bernstein." Do you think David would have felt that he had to change his name if he had read "No Two People Are the Same"? Why or why not? **Possible response: If David had realized that he was already different from everyone else, he might not have felt that he had to change his name to be different.**

3. In "The Big Orange Splot," Mr. Plumbean's neighbors did not understand why he painted his house in such a strange way. How do you think Miss Rumphius would have felt about Mr. Plumbean's house if she had been one of his neighbors? Explain your answer. **Possible response: Miss Rumphius knew how important it was to bring some beauty to the world. She probably would have understood why Mr. Plumbean painted his house differently.**

Interest Inventory

Stories and storytellers are very important. What kind of stories do you enjoy the most? Answer the questions below and use the chart to discover books that you may find especially interesting.

yes no

1. ☐ ☐ Do you enjoy Native American folktales?
2. ☐ ☐ Would you like a funny story with a problem to solve?
3. ☐ ☐ Do you find animal adventures exciting?
4. ☐ ☐ Does a good bedtime story sound interesting?
5. ☐ ☐ Do you like stories told by grandparents about the past?
6. ☐ ☐ Would you like to read stories from faraway places?
7. ☐ ☐ Do you think make-believe stories are fun to read?

Now find the numbers for the questions you checked YES. Follow the column down. When you see a star, move across the row to find the book title. That's the book for you!

1	2	3	4	5	6	7	Title/Author
	★	★			★	★	*Anatole and the Cat* by Eve Titus
		★	★			★	*How Night Came* by Joanna Troughton
★			★				*My Grandmother's Cookie Jar* by Montzalle Miller
	★		★	★		★	*We Can't Sleep* by James Stevenson
					★	★	*A Sunflower as Big as the Sun* by Shan Ellentuck
	★	★				★	*I Had Trouble in Getting to Solla Sollew* by Dr. Seuss
★					★	★	*The Dancing Stars, an Iroquois Legend* by Anne Rockwell

Personal Book List

NAME _____

Title _____

Author _____

Title _____

Author _____

Title _____

Author _____

Title _____

Author _____

Figurative Language

> **REMEMBER: Figurative language** is a special use of words.
> Writers may compare things that are alike in one way but
> different in every other way. Figurative language can help you
> see things in a new and exciting way.

A. Read each sentence in the first column. Write the letter of the
sentence on the right that has a similar meaning.

1. The miller's daughter was as timid
   as a mouse. __f__

2. Her tears filled the room. __e__

3. The little man was as sly as a
   fox. __g__

4. The gold was as dazzling as the
   sun. __c__

5. The queen's messengers scoured
   the countryside. __a__

6. The little man's face clouded
   over. __d__

7. The queen's heart was in her
   mouth. __b__

a. They looked all over.

b. She was very worried.

c. It shone very brightly.

d. He looked upset.

e. She cried a great deal.

f. She was shy and scared.

g. He was sneaky.

B. On separate paper, write a sentence that tells how happy
the queen was at the end of the story. Use a comparison
in your sentence. See Teacher Notes.

Predicting Outcomes

> **REMEMBER:** When you **predict,** you make a guess about what will happen in a story. Use story clues and what you know to make a good prediction.

A. Read each paragraph and guess what will happen next. Write your answer. Then underline the story clues that helped you.

1. Ms. Marple is a storyteller at the library. Children love to listen to her stories. She uses puppets and other things to tell her stories. All the children are sitting on chairs at the library. They are waiting for Ms. Marple to start.

What will happen next? <u>Ms. Marple will tell a story.</u>

2. The children are anxious for Ms. Marple to begin the story. First, they watch Ms. Marple as she reaches into a bag that is next to her chair. Then they watch as she pulls out some straw, some twigs, and a brick. Next she takes out a puppet of a pig.

What will happen next? <u>Ms. Marple will tell a story about a pig.</u>

Ms. Marple will tell the story "The Three Little Pigs."

3. Ms. Marple finished her story about the three little pigs. The children loved it. Then she told them they would make their own finger puppets of a pig with paper. She asked the children to go to the art room.

What will happen next? The children will make their own puppets.

B. Think about a story that Ms. Marple could tell and the things she could use to tell it. On separate paper, write three sentences giving clues that will help someone guess the name of the story.
See Teacher Notes.

Using New Words

A. Read each group of words. Write a word from the box that fits in each group.

bind	calabash	furious	hornets
leopard	phrases	price	

1. tiger   lion   jaguar   _leopard_

2. cost   value   money   _price_

3. glass   cup   container   _calabash_

4. words   sentences   paragraphs   _phrases_

5. tie   secure   knot   _bind_

6. bees   wasps   flies   _hornets_

7. angry   mad   upset   _furious_

B. Read the following paragraph. Then use the words from the box to complete it.

The other day I got a most unusual catalog. It had pictures of strange things to buy and word _phrases_ that told about each one. For a low _price_ , I could buy a _calabash_ from Africa. A pet _leopard_ was more costly and looked dangerous. Insect lovers could buy a nest of _hornets_ . I think my parents would be _furious_ if I bought things from this crazy catalog.

C. On separate paper, write an advertisement that might appear in the catalog. Use at least three words from the box in your ad. See Teacher Notes.

A STORY, A STORY

A. Complete the summary of the story "A Story, A Story."
Accept reasonable variations.

This story is about Ananse and Nyame, who were also called

_____the spider man and the Sky God_____ .

The story comes from ____Africa____ .

At one time, all the ____stories____ belonged to Nyame.

Ananse wanted to buy the stories so he spun a ____web____ up to
the sky. When Nyame heard what Ananse wanted, he laughed that such
a little man would think he could pay his price. The Sky God told the

spider man to bring him the ____leopard____ -of-the-terrible-teeth,

the ____hornet____ who-stings-like-fire, and the fairy-whom-
men-never-see.

First Ananse found the leopard. He got the leopard to play a game

with him called the ____binding binding game____ .
In the game, Ananse tricked the leopard and tied his feet with vines.
Then Ananse found the hornets. He tricked them by telling them it was

____raining____ . They flew into Ananse's calabash to get out
of the rain, and Ananse trapped them by covering its mouth. Last he
went to get the fairy creature. To trick her, he set out a doll covered

with ____sticky gum____ . When the fairy got mad at the
lifeless doll, the fairy hit it and got trapped by the sticky gum. That is
how the spider man caught all three creatures.

The spider man brought them to Nyame. Nyame praised little
Ananse. That is how Ananse got the stories and how they came to be

called ____Spider Stories____ .

B. Imagine you are Ananse. On separate paper, write a story that
tells how you would capture one of the three creatures in "A
Story, A Story." See Teacher Notes.

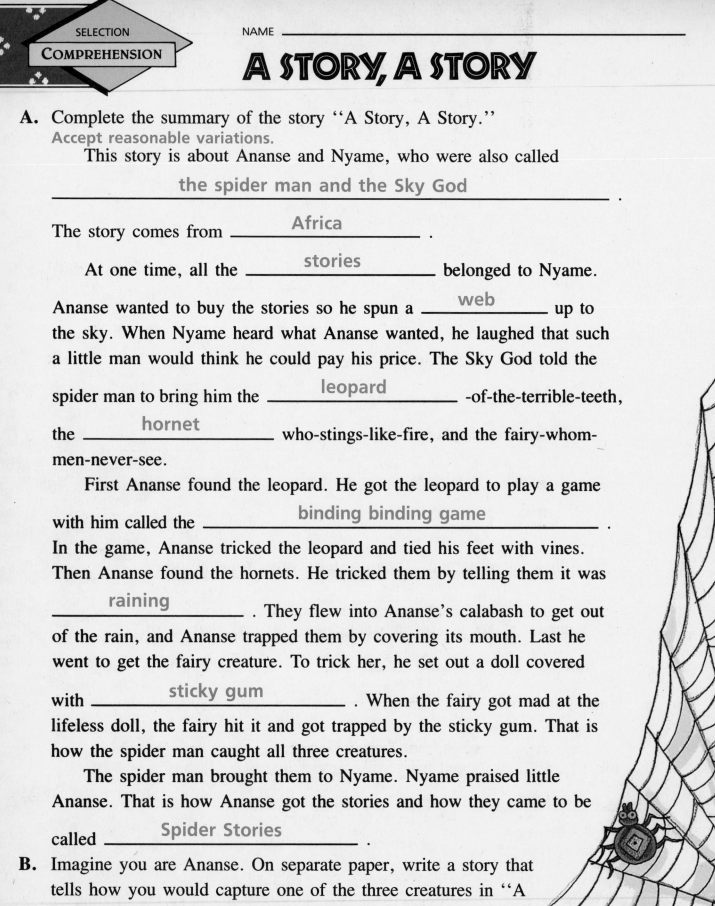

Following Directions

> **REMEMBER: Directions** are steps for doing something. When following directions, read or listen carefully, do the steps in the correct order, and do not skip any steps.

A. Here are the steps for catching a fairy. Write them in order.

1. After the doll is carved, cover it with sticky gum.
2. Finally tie an end of a vine around the doll's head.
3. Then put the sticky doll with the bowl of yams beside a tree.
4. First carve a little wooden doll holding a bowl.

4. First carve a little wooden doll holding a bowl.
_____

1. After the doll is carved, cover it with sticky gum.
_____

3. Then put the sticky doll with the bowl of yams beside a tree.
_____

2. Finally tie an end of a vine around the doll's head.
_____

B. Here are the steps Ananse followed to get his wish from the Sky God. The steps are not in order. Write them in order.

1. Then catch a leopard, some hornets, and a fairy.
2. Finally take them to the Sky God.
3. First go to the Sky God and tell your wish.
4. Next listen to what you must do for the Sky God.

3. First go to the Sky God and tell your wish.
_____

4. Next listen to what you must do for the Sky God.
_____

1. Then catch a leopard, some hornets, and a fairy.
_____

2. Finally take them to the Sky God.
_____

C. On separate paper, write two ways to catch some hornets.
See Teacher Notes.

NAME

Predicting Outcomes

REMEMBER: When you **predict,** you make a guess about what will happen in a story. Use story clues and what you know to make a good prediction.

A. As you read each part of the story, predict what will happen next.

1. Ananse sometimes took the form of a spider. He used his webs to climb up and down the tree where he lived. Each morning, Ananse would start a new web. He liked to choose a sunny spot so he would be warm as he rested each afternoon.

   One day, Ananse woke up and started his web. He spun the thin thread and put it on the first branch. Then he crossed over to another branch to put the thread there. He went on to another branch and was almost finished with the outside ring of the web. Suddenly, one branch snapped. Ananse could feel the web lose its tight, strong shape.

Predict what will happen to Ananse and the web. The web will break, and Ananse will fall.

2. Ananse jumped from the broken web to a nearby stick. Then he carefully made his way down the tree trunk. He would rest for a little while and then climb back up to start a new web.

   Ananse settled down in the center of a fallen leaf. The leaf was on the ground in the sun so Ananse felt warm as he closed his eyes. Over his head, a hungry bird spotted Ananse.

Predict what the bird will do. He will try to eat Ananse.

B. Imagine a fight between Ananse and a mysterious insect. On separate paper, describe the fight and predict who will win. Then tell why you made this prediction. See Teacher Notes.

Inference

REMEMBER: Use story clues and what you already know to figure out things that the writer did not state.

A. Read the sentences. Use clues to figure out the answers to the questions. Write your answers.

1. Ananse walked along a path past huge trees and large plants. He heard monkeys screaming and a leopard growling. **Possible responses:**

Where was Ananse? **He was in the jungle.** _____

2. High in a tree, an animal moved. Ananse could hear its wings beating. Then he heard chirping and saw a feather fall.

What animal was in the tree? **A bird was in the tree.** _____

3. Ananse looked up. The moon and stars were bright in the

black sky. What time was it? **It was night.** _____

4. When the doll did not answer, the fairy yelled at it. When it still didn't answer, the fairy slapped it.

How was the fairy feeling? **It was angry.** _____

5. Ananse rubbed himself with soap and water. Then he dried himself.

What was Ananse doing? **He was bathing.** _____

6. The leopard had not eaten in days. When he saw Ananse, all he could think of was how good Ananse would taste.

How was the leopard feeling? **He was hungry.** _____

B. Choose an object in your classroom. On separate paper, write a list of clues that would help someone guess what the object is. Don't name the object. **See Teacher Notes.**

NAME _____

Using New Words

A. Use the words in the box to complete the story. Write one word on each line.

> earns   expressions   goodie bag
> professional   workshops

My father _____*earns*_____ money by telling stories

to people. He became a _____*professional*_____ storyteller

when people began paying to hear his tales. Dad loves stories. He was

surprised that his stories were well liked by other people.

At _____*workshops*_____ , Dad teaches other people to

tell stories. He shows them how to change the

_____*expressions*_____ on their faces to make a story more

exciting. My dad shows how the special things he puts in his

_____*goodie bag*_____ help him tell a story. One thing he

cannot teach is how his imagination works.

B. Think of a story you would like to tell. On separate paper, write three sentences telling how you would get ready. Use at least three words from the box. **See Teacher Notes.**

The Traveling Storyteller

A. Complete the summary of "The Traveling Storyteller."
Accept reasonable variations.

Linda Goss is a _____storyteller_____ who grew up in

the state of _____Tennessee_____ near the Great Smoky

Mountains. She has told stories in many places in all her travels.

Linda Goss grew up in a storytelling family. The stories that

influenced her most were ones her _____grandfather_____ told

her about Brer Rabbit.

In 1973, Linda Goss became a _____professional_____

storyteller, or someone who earns a living telling stories. Linda lived in

Washington, D.C., where her husband taught at Howard University. He

told her the university was looking for a storyteller. At first Linda was

scared about telling her stories to _____strangers_____ . But

the audience clapped when she was finished.

When Linda moved to Philadelphia, she taught school and often

told her _____students_____ stories. Soon other schools asked

her to tell stories to their students. She traveled to different places

and became a _____traveling_____ storyteller.

Linda uses stories from many different places. Many of her favorites

are folktales from Ghana, a country in _____Africa_____ . To

make the stories exciting, Linda begins by ringing _____bells_____ .

She uses her arms and hands and has a "goodie bag" full of

_____cloths_____ to help her tell stories.

B. On separate paper, write two sentences telling about the kind of
person you think would make a good storyteller. See Teacher Notes.

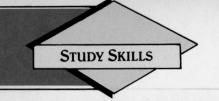
Following Directions

> **REMEMBER: Directions** are steps for doing something. When following directions, read or listen carefully, do the steps in the correct order, and do not skip any steps.

A. Study the map. Follow the set of directions. Then answer the questions.

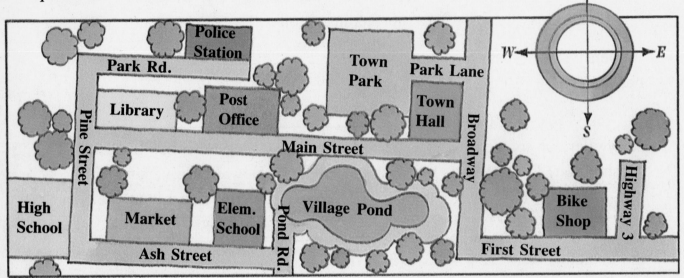

Directions to the Storytelling Contest

Start at the elementary school. Go west on Ash Street until you reach Pine Street. Turn north on Pine Street and travel to Main Street. Go east on Main Street until you reach Broadway. Go north on Broadway. The contest is being held at the town hall.

1. Where do the directions begin? _at the elementary school_

2. On which street will you walk east? _Main Street_

3. What four streets run north and south? _Pine Street, Pond Rd., Broadway, and Highway 3_

4. Where is the contest being held? _the town hall_

B. On separate paper, draw your own map. Underneath, give directions to show how to get from one place to another. See Teacher Notes.

Making a Topic Map

> **REMEMBER:** You can understand a story better and tell whether or not an author is staying on the topic by making a topic map.

A. Read the paragraphs below. As you read, think about the sentences or details that belong with the topic. Write the details on the lines to complete the topic map.

Fun Ways to Tell a Story

After you have learned a story by heart and practiced telling it many times, you can add some special things to your storytelling.

You can use puppets to tell the story. You can make large pictures of different story settings for your listeners to look at as you tell the story.

You can also dress up like the characters in the story and try to change your voice as different characters speak. This will help your listeners remember the characters better.

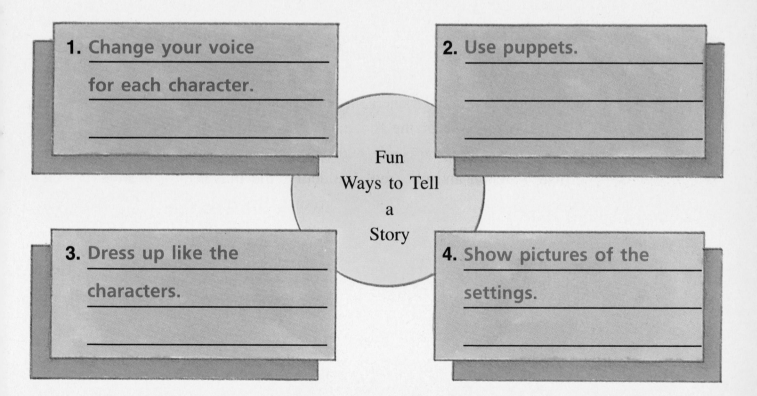

1. Change your voice for each character.

2. Use puppets.

Fun Ways to Tell a Story

3. Dress up like the characters.

4. Show pictures of the settings.

B. Make up one more detail that belongs with this topic. On separate paper, write the topic and your detail. See Teacher Notes.

Checkpoint

Read the paragraphs. Then fill in the circle beside the correct answer.

Once there was a girl who ran as fast as the wind. Speedy Sue would often race cars, trains, and planes for fun. She never lost a race. Sometimes she ran so fast that she got where she was going before anyone knew she had left where she had been. She could run away while someone was talking to her and get back before they could say the next word. Sue was also the pitcher on her baseball team.

One day, Sue's team was winning by one run. The other team had players on all the bases, but there were two outs. Sue pitched to the batter, who hit the ball hard. The sound of the bat hitting the ball was like a crack of thunder. The crowd roared. Somewhere a person screamed and another cried out. The batter threw down the bat and ran. The ball flew like a rocket far over the field. It rose toward the clouds past a frightened bird. At first, it looked like it would go over the fence. Then it started to fall. An outfielder on Sue's team ran to catch it. The crowd watched and cheered. Suddenly, the player tripped and fell. She lay on the ground like a turtle on its back. She couldn't seem to get up. The ball still fell. It looked like Sue's team would lose the game.

1. What will happen next in the story?

   (a) Sue's team will lose.

   (b) Sue will run after the ball and catch it.

   (c) The ball will hit the fence.

   (d) Sue will leave the team.

2. Which sentence from the story helped you decide how the story would end?

   (a) One day, Sue's team was winning by one run.

   (b) Suddenly, the player tripped and fell.

   (c) Once there was a girl who ran as fast as the wind.

   (d) Sue was also the pitcher on her baseball team.

3. The author compares Sue's speed to _____ .

   (a) cars

   (b) trains

   (c) the wind

   (d) planes

4. The author compares the sound of the bat hitting the ball to _____ .

   (a) a scream

   (b) a cry

   (c) a roar

   (d) a crack of thunder

5. The author compares the ball to _____ .

   (a) a bird

   (b) a rocket

   (c) a cloud

   (d) the wind

6. The author compares the player who fell to _____ .

   (a) a rocket

   (b) a turtle

   (c) a ball

   (d) Speedy Sue

NAME

Cause/Effect

> **REMEMBER:** Use signal words, story clues, and what you already know to figure out which events caused other events to happen.

A. Read the paragraph. Fill in the causes and effects.

Storytelling has always been an important part of Linda Goss's life. Because her family loved stories, she grew up with storytelling. As a result of her deep love of storytelling, she decided to become a professional storyteller. She thought she would like to share her stories with the world. She started telling stories to strangers in 1973. The first time she saw all the people in the audience looking at her, she became scared. Soon, however, she forgot that she was scared. The audience liked the way she told stories, so they clapped. Linda felt great.

1. Cause: Her family loved stories.

Effect: ___She grew up with storytelling.___

2. Cause: She had a deep love of storytelling.

Effect: ___She decided to become a professional storyteller.___

3. Cause: ___She saw all the people in the audience looking at her.___

Effect: She became scared.

4. Cause: ___The audience liked the way she told stories.___

Effect: The people clapped.

B. Imagine that the usual story hour at your library has just been canceled. Think of three possible causes for this change. Write your ideas on separate paper. See Teacher Notes.

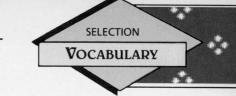

Using New Words

A. Complete each sentence by writing a word from the box.

gasped	groceries	interrupted	ruined	shrugged

Our last surprise party for our mother was a big success. When Mom

came in the door carrying two bags of _____groceries_____ ,

we all yelled, "Surprise!" Mom _____gasped_____

loudly and dropped both bags on the floor. We all began to sing when

she _____interrupted_____ us and pointed to the floor. We

could see that the eggs had broken and that some other things were

also _____ruined_____ . We were scared that she would

be angry. But she smiled, _____shrugged_____ her

shoulders, and said that she was too surprised and happy to care about a

few broken eggs.

B. Write each word from the box next to its meaning.

1. _____groceries_____ household supplies

2. _____interrupted_____ broke in on someone talking

3. _____gasped_____ breathed in suddenly

4. _____shrugged_____ drew up the shoulders

5. _____ruined_____ damaged

C. On separate paper, write a sentence of your own
for each of the words in the box. See Teacher Notes.

Nothing Much Happened Today

A. Complete the summary of "Nothing Much Happened Today."
Accept reasonable variations.

This story is about _____Mrs. Maeberry_____ and her children
and the day that nothing much happened. The story takes place mostly in
the _____kitchen_____ of the house.

On her way home from the store, Mrs. Maeberry saw the police
chasing a _____robber_____ . She saw millions of
_____soap bubbles_____ drifting from the front window. She ran
inside to ask her children what had happened. The reply was "Nothing
much, really." This is the story she heard bit by bit. Only she heard
it from end to beginning.

While Mrs. Maeberry was gone, the police officer chased the robber
into the kitchen and knocked over a _____cake_____ she had made
earlier. The cake fell to the floor, and the robber slipped on
the _____icing_____ . The children decided to bake a new cake, but it
spilled in the oven, and the kitchen got smoky. When they opened
a _____window_____ , a cat jumped into the room. The _____dog_____
chased the cat and knocked a sack of _____sugar_____ on himself. The
children gave the dog a bath but used too many suds. That's why soap
bubbles started going out the window.

Mrs. Maeberry wondered how so much could happen in such a short
time. The children saw things _____differently_____ . They told her nothing
much had happened and asked her about her day.

B. Think about a silly chain of events. On separate paper, write three sentences
describing the chain of events. **See Teacher Notes.**

Figurative Language

REMEMBER: Figurative language is a special use of words. Writers may compare things that are alike in one way but different in every other way. Figurative language can help you see things in a new and exciting way.

A. Write a word from the box to complete each example of figurative language.

cave	coal	fish	mud	needles
oranges	rock	sky	snow	

1. The cake the children burned was as black as _____ coal _____ .

2. Some of the bubbles from the suds were as big as _____ oranges _____ .

3. The sugar fell like _____ snow _____ when Popsicle knocked it down.

4. The police officer's coat was as blue as the _____ sky _____ .

5. Everyone knew that Allan's head was as hard as a _____ rock _____ .

6. The heavy smoke made the room as dark as a _____ cave _____ .

7. Mrs. Maeberry gasped like a _____ fish _____ out of water.

8. The icing from the ruined cake made the kitchen floor as slippery as _____ mud _____ .

9. The strange cat's teeth were as sharp as _____ needles _____ .

B. On separate paper, use comparisons to describe the look of snow. See Teacher Notes.

COMPREHENSION

Author's Purpose

REMEMBER: As you read, ask yourself if an author is writing to entertain you or to inform you.

A. Read each paragraph. To tell the author's purpose, write *to entertain* or *to inform* after each paragraph.

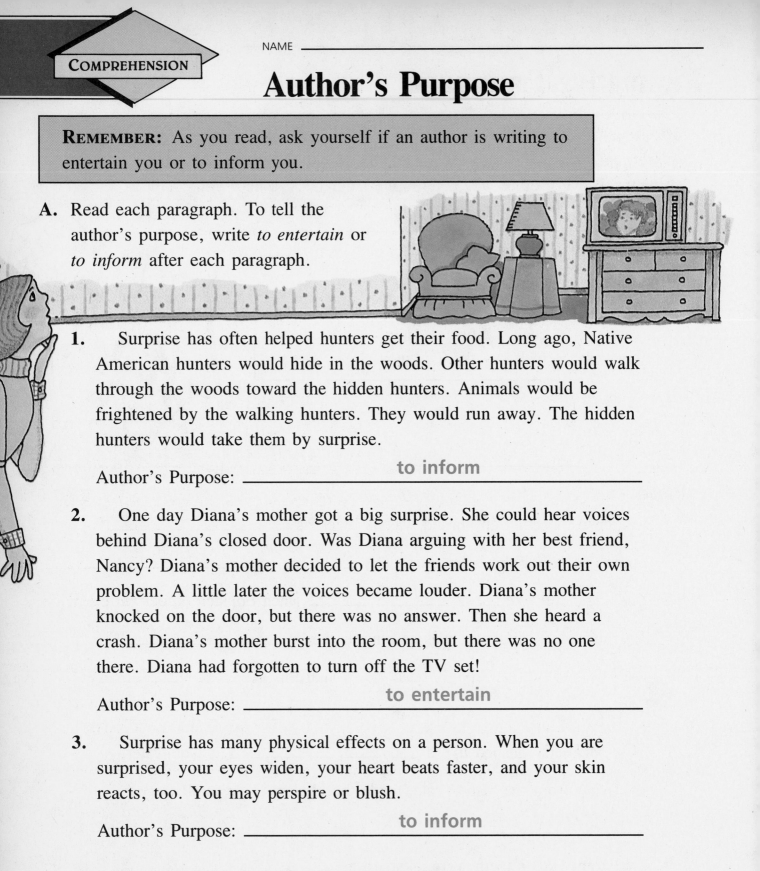

1. Surprise has often helped hunters get their food. Long ago, Native American hunters would hide in the woods. Other hunters would walk through the woods toward the hidden hunters. Animals would be frightened by the walking hunters. They would run away. The hidden hunters would take them by surprise.

   Author's Purpose: _____ to inform _____

2. One day Diana's mother got a big surprise. She could hear voices behind Diana's closed door. Was Diana arguing with her best friend, Nancy? Diana's mother decided to let the friends work out their own problem. A little later the voices became louder. Diana's mother knocked on the door, but there was no answer. Then she heard a crash. Diana's mother burst into the room, but there was no one there. Diana had forgotten to turn off the TV set!

   Author's Purpose: _____ to entertain _____

3. Surprise has many physical effects on a person. When you are surprised, your eyes widen, your heart beats faster, and your skin reacts, too. You may perspire or blush.

   Author's Purpose: _____ to inform _____

B. On separate paper, write a list of books that you would use to find information. Then tell what kind of information each book offers. See Teacher Notes.

Predicting Outcomes

REMEMBER: When you **predict,** you make a guess about what will happen in a story. Use story clues and what you know to make a good prediction.

A. Read each paragraph. Then write a prediction about what will happen next.

1. The family dog, Mittens, did not like to be bathed. He would run away whenever anyone tried to wash him. One day, the children tried to wash him.

    What will Mittens do? _He will run away._

2. Father baked some bread. Mother fixed some vegetable stew. Then they told everyone dinner was ready.

    What will everyone have for dinner? _bread and vegetable stew_

3. Rosa found her baseball glove and bat. She asked her brother Henry if he had the baseball.

    What will Rosa and Henry do? _play baseball_

4. The storm had blown leaves all over the yard. Some branches had even fallen on the ground. Mother had an outdoor job for Frank.

    What will Frank do? _clean up the yard_

5. Stan told his mother that his school was having a bake sale. Each child was supposed to bring something to sell. Stan's mother was a good baker.

    What will Stan ask his mother? _He will ask her to bake something._

B. Imagine that you are a weather reporter. On separate paper, write some of the clues that would help you predict that it was going to rain. See Teacher Notes.

Using New Words

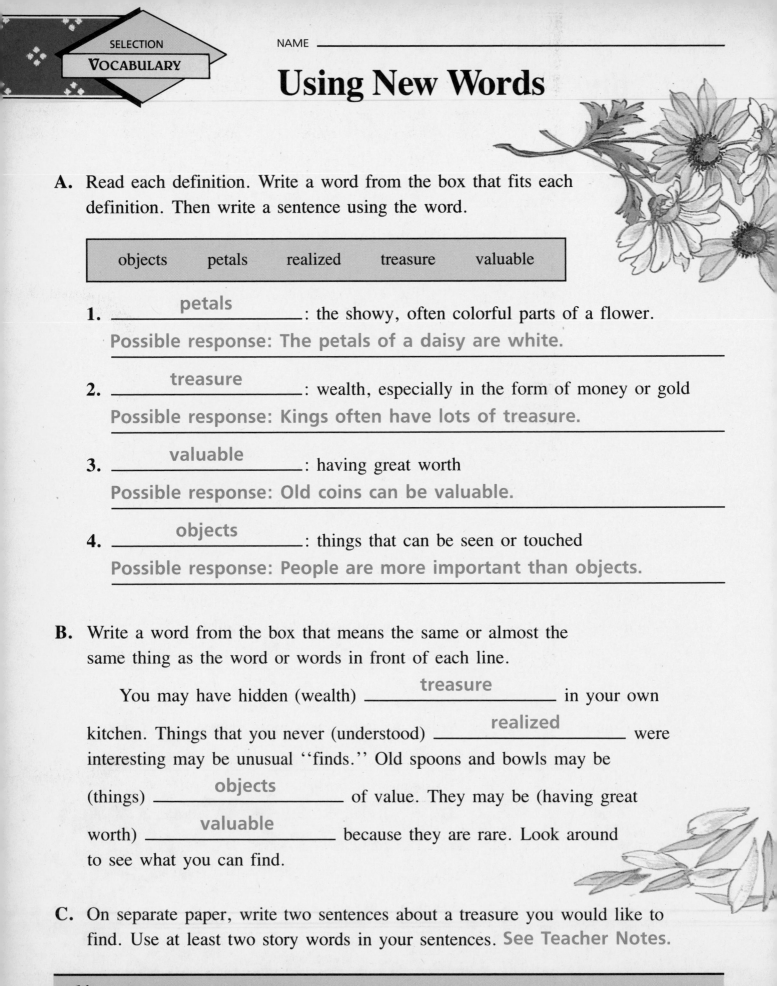

A. Read each definition. Write a word from the box that fits each definition. Then write a sentence using the word.

objects	petals	realized	treasure	valuable

1. _____petals_____: the showy, often colorful parts of a flower.

   Possible response: The petals of a daisy are white.

2. _____treasure_____: wealth, especially in the form of money or gold

   Possible response: Kings often have lots of treasure.

3. _____valuable_____: having great worth

   Possible response: Old coins can be valuable.

4. _____objects_____: things that can be seen or touched

   Possible response: People are more important than objects.

B. Write a word from the box that means the same or almost the same thing as the word or words in front of each line.

You may have hidden (wealth) _____treasure_____ in your own

kitchen. Things that you never (understood) _____realized_____ were interesting may be unusual ''finds.'' Old spoons and bowls may be

(things) _____objects_____ of value. They may be (having great

worth) _____valuable_____ because they are rare. Look around to see what you can find.

C. On separate paper, write two sentences about a treasure you would like to find. Use at least two story words in your sentences. See Teacher Notes.

King Midas and the Golden Touch

A. Complete the summary of "King Midas and the Golden Touch."
Accept reasonable variations.

This story is about a rich king named _____Midas_____ and his

daughter _____Marygold_____ . The story takes place at the

_____castle_____ . The king loved two things very much,

_____money/gold_____ and his daughter. One day in his

treasure room, a stranger appeared. Midas told the stranger he wished that

_____everything he touched would turn to gold_____ . The stranger

promised that the king's wish would come true the next day.

In the morning, Midas touched his water jug. At once it

_____turned to gold_____ . The same thing happened to his

clothes and the roses he touched on the way to breakfast. When

Marygold arrived at breakfast, she was _____crying_____ because

all the roses had turned to gold. Then the king's food turned to gold.

Marygold hurried to comfort her father, but when she touched him, she

_____turned to gold, too_____ .

Midas felt very sad. Then he looked up and saw the stranger. Midas

made a new wish. He wished that _____he could get rid_____

_____of his terrible gift_____ .

The stranger told him to wash in the river and to splash water on
everything that had turned gold. Midas splashed the water on everything
he had turned to gold. Then the king woke up.

Years later, Midas told Marygold's children about his _____dream_____ .
He told them the gold in their hair was the only gold he valued now.

B. On separate paper, write three sentences to describe what you
would wish for if a stranger gave you one wish. See Teacher Notes.

NAME _____

Figurative Language

> **REMEMBER: Figurative language** is a special use of words. Writers may compare things that are alike in one way but different in every other way. Figurative language can help you see things in a new and exciting way.

A. Read the sentences. What is each underlined thing being compared to? Write your answer.

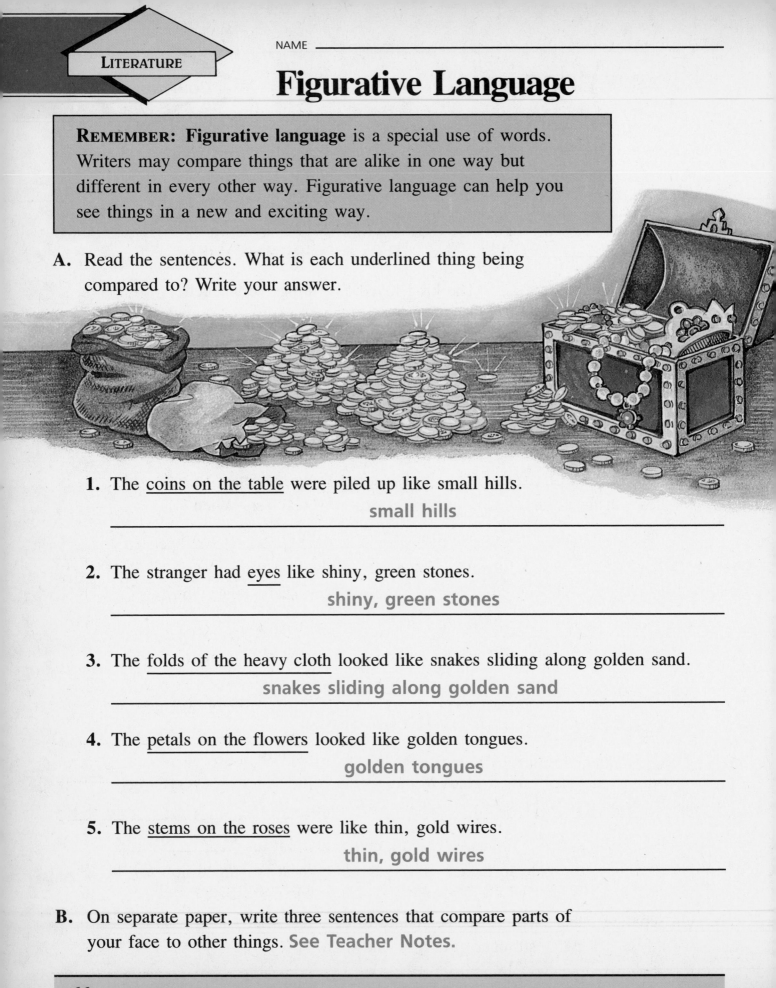

1. The <u>coins on the table</u> were piled up like small hills.

small hills

_____

2. The stranger had <u>eyes</u> like shiny, green stones.

shiny, green stones

_____

3. The <u>folds of the heavy cloth</u> looked like snakes sliding along golden sand.

snakes sliding along golden sand

_____

4. The <u>petals on the flowers</u> looked like golden tongues.

golden tongues

_____

5. The <u>stems on the roses</u> were like thin, gold wires.

thin, gold wires

_____

B. On separate paper, write three sentences that compare parts of your face to other things. See Teacher Notes.

Following Directions

> **REMEMBER: Directions** are steps for doing something. When following directions, read or listen carefully, do the steps in the correct order, and do not skip any steps.

A. Study the picture of King Midas's castle grounds. Then write four steps that tell King Midas how to get from the castle to the river. You may use words from the box to help you.

across	beside	down
first	next	over
past	then	through

Possible answers may include:

1. First walk down the hill from the castle.

2. Next open the gate and go through it.

3. Walk across the road.

4. Go down another path to the river.

B. Think about how you would write directions for leaving your classroom and going to the principal's office. On separate paper, write the directions. Number the steps. Write at least three steps. See Teacher Notes.

Characterization

REMEMBER: To understand a character, think about what the character says and does. Also, think about how the character speaks and acts.

A. Read about the characters' actions and words. Write the word that tells what the character was like.

1. "If I had my way, everything I touched would turn into gold," Midas said.

   thoughtful   greedy

   _____ greedy _____

2. Midas went out into the garden and touched rosebush after rosebush to turn them to gold.

   greedy   fearless

   _____ greedy _____

3. Marygold could see that Midas was unhappy when his food turned to gold, and she hurried to comfort her father.

   thoughtful   athletic

   _____ thoughtful _____

4. When Marygold turned to gold, Midas said, "Oh, what a terrible thing I have done!"

   worried   daring

   _____ worried _____

B. On separate paper, write a letter to Marygold. Tell her what you think of her father. See Teacher Notes.

Using New Words

A. Use the words in the box to complete the story. Write the word that means the same as the word or words under each line.

bamboos	desolate	harmony	imagination	imperial	scroll

Little Ling lost his favorite toy. He felt _____**desolate**_____.
(very sad)
Ling went outside.

Little Ling walked on the path. He could hear the wind make

the _____**bamboos**_____ sway back and forth. He could feel
(tall plants with hollow stems)
the sun on his back. The warm sun and the quiet sound of

the wind made everything feel in _____**harmony**_____.
(pleasing arrangement of things)
From the path Ling could see a shape like a roll of paper. He

carefully pulled the _____**scroll**_____ from a place near
(roll of paper with a message)
the rocks. Then he unrolled it. There was a picture of some hills. On

one of them was an _____**imperial**_____ palace.
(royal)
Little Ling smiled. He wanted to tell his family about the scroll. As

he walked home, he used his _____**imagination**_____ to think
about the picture on the scroll.   (pictures in the mind)

B. On separate paper, write three sentences describing a scroll or bamboo. Then draw a picture of what you described. See Teacher Notes.

The Emperor's Plum Tree

A. Complete the summary of "The Emperor's Plum Tree."
Accept reasonable variations.

This story is about an _____ emperor _____ who learned wisdom

from a boy. The setting is in the country of ____ Japan ____ .

The emperor walked through his beautiful garden every morning.

One day he found that one of his plum trees ____ was dying ____ .
Only a new tree could make the emperor happy again.

Messengers searched the land for the perfect tree. They found it in
Ukiyo's garden. Ukiyo loved to paint pictures of the tree, and his wife

Tanka wrote ____ poems about it ____ . Most importantly, their

son, Musuko, had a friend, ____ a nightingale ____ , who lived
there. The emperor's wishes came first, however.

As the tree was being taken away, Musuko asked the emperor's

messenger if he could ____ tie a scroll to the tree ____ .
Soon the tree was replanted in the emperor's garden. It was perfect, and
the emperor was happy again. When the emperor saw the scroll on the

tree, he unrolled it and saw a drawing of a branch of the ____ tree ____
and a poem. The poem asked a question. It asked the emperor what to

tell the nightingale when ____ she returned and found no home ____ .

The emperor sent for Ukiyo, Tanka, and Musuko. He told
Musuko to tell the nightingale that her plum tree will be

_____ returned to her _____ by
"the emperor's order." Then the emperor asked Ukiyo to paint a

____ picture ____ of his garden so he could remember it

when it looked perfect.

B. Think about the emperor's beautiful garden. On separate paper,
write three sentences that describe it. See Teacher Notes.

Predicting Outcomes

> **REMEMBER:** When you **predict,** you make a guess about what will happen in a story. Use story clues and what you know to make a good prediction.

A. Read each paragraph. Then predict what the character might do. Use story clues.

1. The emperor loved to walk by the pond near his palace. One day, he looked at some plants near its edge. They were brown and dying. It made the emperor feel sad. He liked it when all the plants looked green and alive. He called a worker over and told him what to do.

    What do you predict the emperor will tell the worker? Possible response: He will tell the worker to remove the dying plants and put in new ones.

2. Little Musuko had a friend. It was the nightingale. Musuko would go out in his garden every night. The nightingale would sing songs to Musuko. The nightingale made Musuko feel happy. One night Musuko could not go out in the garden. He had to go to a party with his family.
    What do you predict the nightingale will do when she doesn't see Musuko?
    Possible reponse: The nightingale will wonder what happened and feel sad. But she may still sing.

    How do you predict Musuko will feel at the party? Possible response: Musuko will feel sad and miss his friend.

B. Imagine the emperor is given a beautiful vase to hold flowers. Then he finds out the vase was taken away from an old woman who misses it. On separate paper, write two sentences that tell what you think the emperor would do. See Teacher Notes.

Checkpoint

Read the paragraph. Look at the map. Then fill in the circle beside the correct answer.

One day, Ananse got a letter telling him about a storytelling contest. The contest was at the library. The letter contained a map showing how to get there. Ananse looked at the map and decided that he would go to some other places as well as the library.

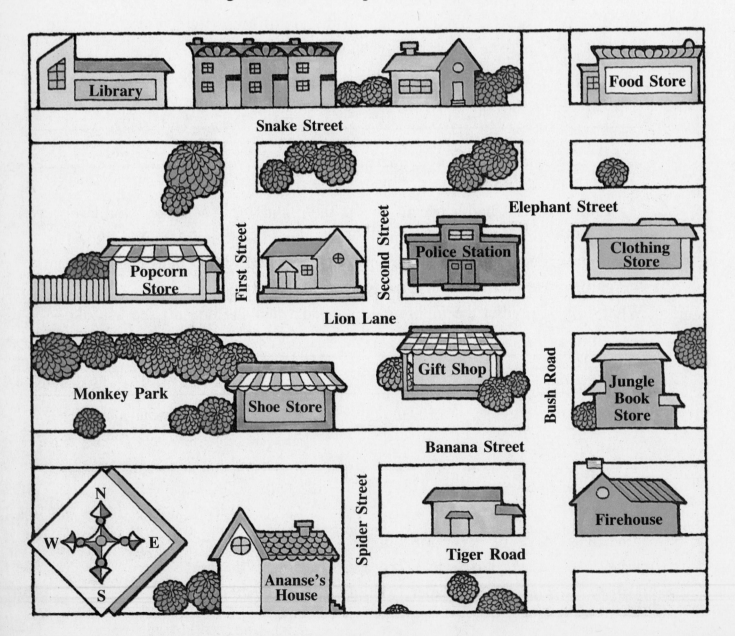

1. Start at Ananse's house. Walk north on Spider Street to Banana Street. Turn right and go east two blocks on Banana Street. What building is on your left?

   (a) Firehouse

   (b) Gift Shop

   (c) Shoe Store

   (d) Jungle Book Store

2. Start outside the Firehouse on Bush Road. Go north two blocks on Bush Road. Turn left on Lion Lane. What building is on your left?

   (a) Jungle Book Store

   (b) Gift Shop

   (c) Clothing Store

   (d) Police Station

3. Start at the Gift Shop on Lion Lane. Walk west two blocks. What building is on your right?

   (a) Popcorn Store

   (b) Gift Shop

   (c) Clothing Store

   (d) Police Station

4. Start at the Gift Shop on Lion Lane. Walk east to Bush Road. Turn left on Bush Road and walk one block north to Elephant Street. Turn right on Elephant Street and walk east. What building is on your right?

   (a) Police Station

   (b) Clothing Store

   (c) Jungle Book Store

   (d) Popcorn Store

5. Start at the Firehouse. Walk north on Bush Road for four blocks. Turn left on Snake Street and walk two blocks west. What building is on your right?

   (a) Library

   (b) Food Store

   (c) Firehouse

   (d) Popcorn Store

6. Start at the corner of Snake Street and Bush Road. Walk south on Bush Road to Banana Street. Turn right and go west two blocks. What is on your right?

   (a) Gift Shop

   (b) Jungle Book Store

    Monkey Park

   (d) Ananse's House

Vocabulary Review

Fill in the circle beside the word that best fits in the sentence.

1. After we buy the food in a store, I help put the _____ away.
   a) workshops
   b) groceries
   c) objects
   d) hornets

2. That large animal with spots is called a _____ .
   a) scroll
   b) calabash
   c) splot
   d) leopard

3. Each flower added to a _____ of color that was pretty to look at.
   a) calabash
   b) harmony
   c) treasure
   d) conservatory

4. The once beautiful _____ of the dying flower fell off one by one.
   a) objects
   b) petals
   c) bamboos
   d) hornets

5. If you found some gold coins, you might think you had discovered a _____ .
   a) treasure
   b) conservatory
   c) retina
   d) scroll

6. Mark didn't care very much about the old hat he had lost, so he _____ his shoulders and walked home.
   a) ruined
   b) realized
   c) persuaded
   d) shrugged

7. Because my uncle is an artist, he really likes to go to _____ where he meets and works with other artists.
   a) workshops
   b) arches
   c) lanes
   d) professional

8. Maria's father earns his living by being a _____ basketball player.
- a) imperial
- **b) professional**
- c) harmony
- d) experiences

9. The king wrote a message to his people on a _____ instead of a sheet of paper.
- **a) scroll**
- b) treasure
- c) splot
- d) calculator

10. The old man lived like a king in a large house that looked like an _____ palace.
- a) unusual
- **b) imperial**
- c) interrupted
- d) icy

11. Large, yellow flying insects that build nests of paper are called _____ .
- a) phrases
- b) expressions
- **c) hornets**
- d) bamboos

12. The heavy rains _____ all the flowers in the garden.
- a) shrugged
- b) gasped
- c) interrupted
- **d) ruined**

13. To keep the box from falling apart, we had to tie it tightly, or _____ it, with rope.
- **a) bind**
- b) identify
- c) plow
- d) relax

14. Kevin keeps his stamp collection in a safe place because it contains many _____ stamps.
- a) professional
- b) desolate
- c) imperial
- **d) valuable**

15. When his daughter became a gold statue, King Midas _____ how little gold meant to him.
- a) shrugged
- **b) realized**
- c) gasped
- d) interrupted

Unit Wrap-Up

NAME _____

Read each question. Write your answer, using complete sentences.

1. How did King Midas in "King Midas and the Golden Touch" and the emperor in "The Emperor's Plum Tree" become wiser as a result of what happened to them? Possible response: Both of them learned that what you think you want is not always the best thing to have.

2. In "A Story, A Story," the author explains that Ananse stories were told on slave ships. Why do you think slaves told stories about small defenseless people who outwitted others and succeeded against great odds? Possible response: The slaves probably felt small and defenseless themselves. These stories might have given them hope and courage.

3. Mrs. Maeberry in "Nothing Much Happened Today" was very confused by the way her children told her the story of what had happened. How do you think a professional storyteller such as Linda Goss would tell the story to make it less confusing? Possible response: A professional storyteller would probably put the story in order and would not tell it in bits and pieces.

Interest Inventory

Some problems are hard to solve. What problems are you good at solving? Answer the questions below and use the chart to discover books that you may find especially interesting.

	yes	no	
1.	☐	☐	Do you like stories about animals who solve problems?
2.	☐	☐	Would you like to see how families figure things out?
3.	☐	☐	Do you enjoy figuring out puzzles?
4.	☐	☐	Has anyone ever helped you figure out something?
5.	☐	☐	Do you like funny tales about jungle animals?
6.	☐	☐	Do you like doing puzzles about everyday things?
7.	☐	☐	Can we help each other by working together?

Now find the numbers for the questions you checked YES. Follow the column down. When you see a star, move across the row to find the book title. That's the book for you!

1	2	3	4	5	6	7	Title/Author
	★	★		★			*Tell Me About Measures* by Alain Grace
★			★				*What Made Tiddalik Laugh* by Joanna Troughton
			★			★	*See You Tomorrow, Charles* by Miriam Cohen
★			★	★			*The Elephant Who Couldn't Forget* by Faith McNulty
★	★					★	*Everyone Ready?* by Franz Brandenburg
★			★			★	*Pop! Goes the Turnip* by Harold Berson
		★	★		★		*Is This a Baby Dinosaur?* by Millicent Selsam

Personal Book List

NAME ———————————————————————————

Title ———————————————————————————

Author ———————————————————————————

Title ———————————————————————————

Author ———————————————————————————

Title ———————————————————————————

Author ———————————————————————————

Title ———————————————————————————

Author ———————————————————————————

Classification

> **REMEMBER:** To **classify** words, decide how they are alike and different in meaning.

A. Read the list of items. Decide whether each item goes best with machines or people. Circle the items that tell about people. Then fill in the chart. One item can be placed in both columns.

1. gears
2. switch
3. motor
4. (heart)
5. (food)
6. electricity
7. (power)
8. (thoughts)
9. (muscles)
10. oil
11. (dreams)

	Machines	**People**
12.	power	dreams
13.	motor	heart
14.	electricity	food
15.	gears	thoughts
16.	oil	muscles
17.	switch	power

B. Think of eight different machines. On a separate paper, write them in two lists with the headings Used for Fun and Used for Work. **See Teacher Notes.**

COMPREHENSION

Drawing Conclusions

> **REMEMBER:** When you **draw a conclusion,** you figure out things that are not explained in a story. Use story clues and what you already know to draw a conclusion.

A. Read the paragraphs. Read the two conclusions. Write the correct one.

1. Jonas couldn't wait to get home from school to change clothes and relax. He needed to change his clothes so he could go over to his friend's house and play.

Jonas walked up the path to his house and reached into his jacket for the key. It wasn't there. He knew his mother was at the dentist's office and would not be home for an hour. Then Jonas remembered his neighbor had an extra key to his house.
We can draw the conclusion that:

    a. Jonas went to the neighbor's to get the extra key.

    b. Jonas went to his friend's without changing his clothes.

a. **Jonas went to the neighbor's to get the extra key.**

2. Mary knew her mother's birthday was coming up in a week. She didn't know what to get, and she didn't have much money.

Mary decided she could at least make a birthday card. Then she had an idea. On the card she could write promises to her mother of things she would do for her. Mary's mother smiled when she opened the card.
We can draw the conclusion that:

    a. Mary brought a gift for her mother that cost a lot of money.

    b. Mary gave her mother a card she made and some special promises.

b. **Mary gave her mother a card she made and some special**

promises.

B. Read the second paragraph again. On separate paper, write your conclusions about the kind of person Mary is. See Teacher Notes.

Using New Words

A. Write a word from the box beside its meaning.

alarm	alert	colonists	hoofbeats	independence	redcoats

1. settlers ___colonists___

2. soldiers ___redcoats___

3. warning ___alarm___

4. warn ___alert___

5. freedom ___independence___

B. Write a word from the box on each line to complete the paragraph.

Many of the ___colonists___ who had settled in North America were not happy. They wanted their ___independence___. They did not want to be told what to do by a king who lived far away, across the ocean. The king became angry. He sent ___redcoats___ to make sure the settlers did not disobey him. Whenever the settlers heard the ___hoofbeats___ of the soldiers' horses, they rang a bell. The bell was an ___alarm___. It was used to ___alert___ people to danger. Life was both dangerous and difficult during this time.

C. Think of some other ways the settlers could have warned each other. On separate paper, tell what they could have done. Use at least three words from the box in your sentences. See Teacher Notes.

Sybil Rides BY NIGHT

A. Complete the summary of "Sybil Rides by Night."
Accept reasonable variations.

This selection is about a girl named _____Sybil_____ and her ride

for independence. The setting is colonial _____New England/Connecticut_____ .

In the year 1777, the _____American_____ colonists were fighting
for their independence from Great Britain. On April 26, Colonel
Ludington learned that the British were burning down a town nearby.
The American soldiers had to be warned. Sybil said she would warn

them by riding to them on her horse named _____Star_____ .

To warn everyone, Sybil would need to ride _____all night long_____ .
Her purpose was to tell the soldiers to come to the Ludington house.

One by one she reached the farmhouses. Sybil shouted

_____her message_____ and rode on. She knew she had done

her job when she heard the _____town bell_____ ringing the alarm.
Her throat hurt from shouting. Once she had to get off the path because

_____she heard British soldiers coming_____ .

Even so, Sybil made sure that all the villages got the message.

When she reached home, the yard was full of soldiers. "Is Danbury
still burning?" asked Sybil, seeing red in the eastern sky. Her father told

her it was _____the sunrise_____ . Years later, Sybil told her

children and her children's children about her ride for

_____independence_____ .

B. Imagine you were an American soldier who rode at night to
Colonel Ludington's house. On separate paper, write three
sentences describing that night and what you saw and felt.
See Teacher Notes.

Drawing Conclusions

> **REMEMBER:** When you **draw a conclusion,** you figure out
> things that are not explained in a story. Use story clues and what
> you already know to draw a conclusion.

A. Read the events that might have happened on Sybil's ride.
Complete each statement.

1. Sybil trembled in the cold night air and pulled her cloak tighter
around her. The wind shook the bushes beside the path and rattled the
branches overhead. "I must keep going," Sybil said to herself, even
though she felt more frightened every second. "I must warn the
soldiers!"

We can draw the conclusion that Sybil was brave because she forced herself
to continue even though the cold, the dark, and the spooky noises

caused her to feel uncomfortable and afraid.

2. Sybil was hungry and was reaching into her pocket for a carrot when
Star slipped. Sybil and Star fell. Sybil got up and checked Star. Then
she felt for the carrot, but it was no longer in her pocket. "Oh, well,"
she thought. "At least Star wasn't badly hurt."

We can draw the conclusion that Sybil was unselfish because even though she
herself fell and even though she was hungry and lost her carrot,

she showed more concern for Star than for herself.

B. On separate paper, write a few sentences about Sybil's adventure
that would lead to the conclusion that Sybil was careful. Don't
use the word *careful*. See Teacher Notes.

Cause/Effect

> **REMEMBER:** Use signal words, story clues, and what you already know to figure out which events caused other events to happen.

A. Read the paragraph. Write each missing cause or effect.

The rider had traveled all day so he was too tired to go on. Since there was no one else to go, Sybil decided to warn the soldiers. As it was late at night, many people were asleep. Sybil banged on their doors. As a result, the people woke up. Sybil rode on. Because she yelled all night, she lost her voice.

1. Cause: The rider had traveled all day.

Effect: _He was too tired to go on._ _____

2. Cause: _There was no one else to go._ _____

Effect: Sybil decided to warn the soldiers.

3. Cause: Sybil banged on people's doors.

Effect: _People woke up._ _____

4. Cause: She yelled all night.

Effect: _She lost her voice._ _____

B. Imagine you left the windows open in your car all night and it rained that night. On separate paper, write one effect this would have on the car and one effect it might have on you. See Teacher Notes.

NAME _____

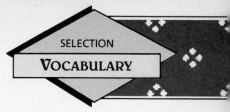

Using New Words

A. Write a word from the box next to each meaning.

advisers	barge	courtiers	herald
informed	intelligence	peasants	prince

1. wise people who give others ideas

1. _____advisers_____

2. told the facts

2. _____informed_____

3. the ability to think and learn

3. _____intelligence_____

4. people at a royal palace

4. _____courtiers_____

5. poor farmers

5. _____peasants_____

6. a large, flat boat built to carry heavy loads

6. _____barge_____

7. person who announces important news

7. _____herald_____

8. the son of a king or queen

8. _____prince_____

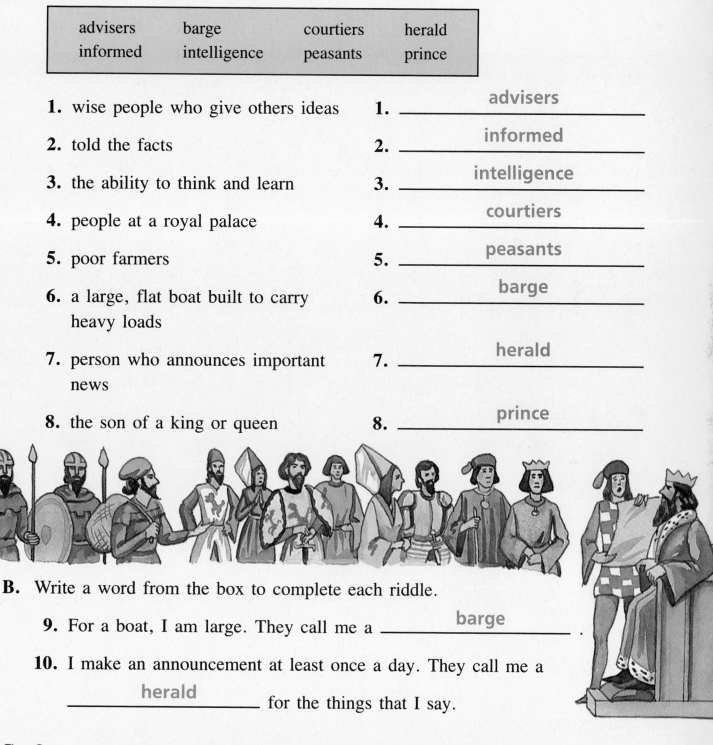

B. Write a word from the box to complete each riddle.

9. For a boat, I am large. They call me a _____barge_____.

10. I make an announcement at least once a day. They call me a _____herald_____ for the things that I say.

C. On separate paper, write three new riddles using the words from the box. Your riddles do not have to rhyme. See Teacher Notes.

8,000 STONES

A. Complete the summary of the story "8,000 Stones."
Accept reasonable variations.

This story is about Ts'ao Ts'ao, the Most Supreme Governor, and

his _____son_____ P'ei. It takes place in the country of

_____China_____ a long time ago.

This governor lived in a beautiful palace. Many kings came to see its

beauty, or they sent messengers with _____presents_____ . The

Satrap of India sent an _____elephant_____ . Ts'ao Ts'ao was

delighted with the gift. First he found out the animal was ten feet tall.

Then he asked its _____weight_____ . No one knew the answer

because no scale was big enough.

All the governor's advisors thought and thought about a way to

weigh the elephant. They couldn't come up with a solution. Little P'ei

asked them what they were doing.

Little P'ei had an idea. He told the advisors to follow him to the

small pond where he sailed his _____boat_____ . He showed them a strange line

carved on its side. He told them that when he sailed the boat with a small,

ivory elephant in it, the boat would sink in the _____water_____ to the line.

"Do the same thing with the big elephant," P'ei said. So they put

the real elephant on a _____barge_____ . P'ei carved an elephant on the

barge's side on the water line. Then they took the elephant off and

piled _____stones_____ on the barge.

And that is how the governor learned that the elephant weighed

_____8,000_____ stones. Everyone cheered because the problem had been

solved by Ts'ao Ts'ao's clever son.

B. Think of a gift you would give the governor. On separate paper,
write three sentences that describe the gift. See Teacher Notes.

Graphs

> **REMEMBER:** A **graph** is a drawing used to present numerical information. Use the caption, key, and labels to help you understand information on graphs.

A. Read the bar graph. Answer the questions.

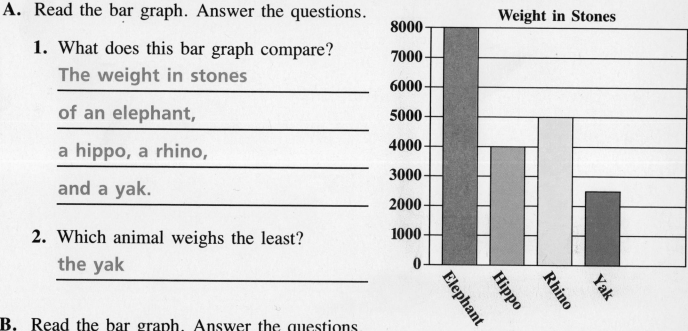

1. What does this bar graph compare?

The weight in stones

of an elephant,

a hippo, a rhino,

and a yak.

2. Which animal weighs the least?

the yak

B. Read the bar graph. Answer the questions.

3. Which female elephant is the taller? _____ African

4. Which male elephant is the shorter? _____ Asian

C. Keep a record of the number of students present in your class for three days. On separate paper, put the information on a bar graph. See Teacher Notes.

Classification

REMEMBER: To **classify** words, decide how they are alike and different in meaning.

A. Write each word from the box under the correct heading.

banner	crown	elephant	governor
king	lake	lion	pond
prince	river	throne	tiger

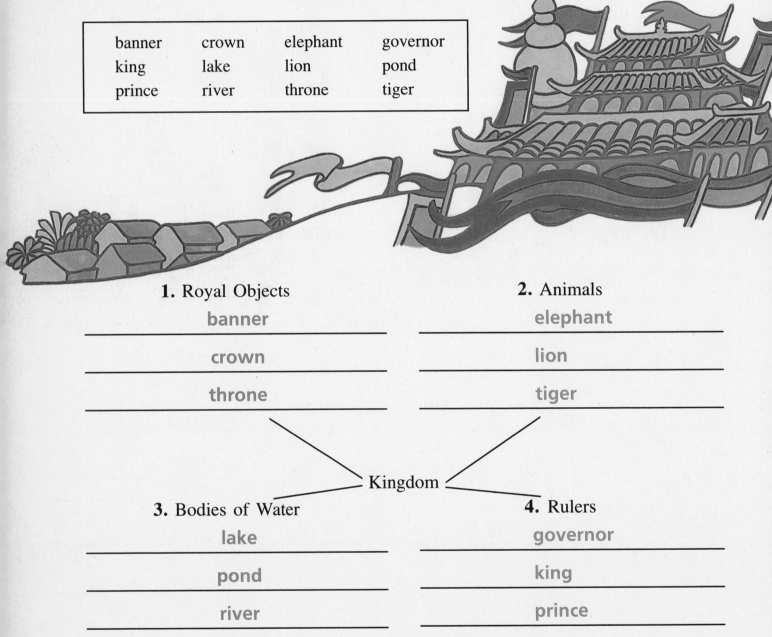

1. Royal Objects

banner

crown

throne

2. Animals

elephant

lion

tiger

Kingdom

3. Bodies of Water

lake

pond

river

4. Rulers

governor

king

prince

B. Look at the word map for Kingdom. Think of two other words that you could add to each group. On separate paper, make a new word map using your words. **See Teacher Notes.**

Main Idea/Details

REMEMBER: A **main idea** tells the topic of the paragraph and what the paragraph says about the topic.

A. Read each paragraph. Write the sentence that tells the main idea of the paragraph.

1. A barge is a special kind of boat. Most large boats have sails or motors to move them through the water. A barge has no motor or sails. It is meant to be pushed by another boat. While other boats usually carry people, barges are made to carry only things.

Main Idea: A barge is a special kind of boat.

2. Elephants can use their trunks as well as their legs to move things. They are the largest of all the animals living on land, and they are very strong. Because of this, they can pull heavier loads than other animals. Sometimes they are used to push over trees or to lift stones. The elephant is an animal that works very hard.

Main Idea: The elephant is an animal that works very hard.

3. The royal gardens were given a lot of care. Each and every day workers would water the plants there. They would carefully cut the bushes and the grass. They even took away the dead flowers before these could fall to the ground and spoil the gardens' beauty.

Main Idea: The royal gardens were given a lot of care.

B. On separate paper, write a paragraph about your favorite game or hobby. Make sure one sentence in the paragraph states your main idea. See Teacher Notes.

NAME _____

Using New Words

A. Write a word from the box to complete each sentence.

balance	measurement	ounce
temperature	thermometer	units

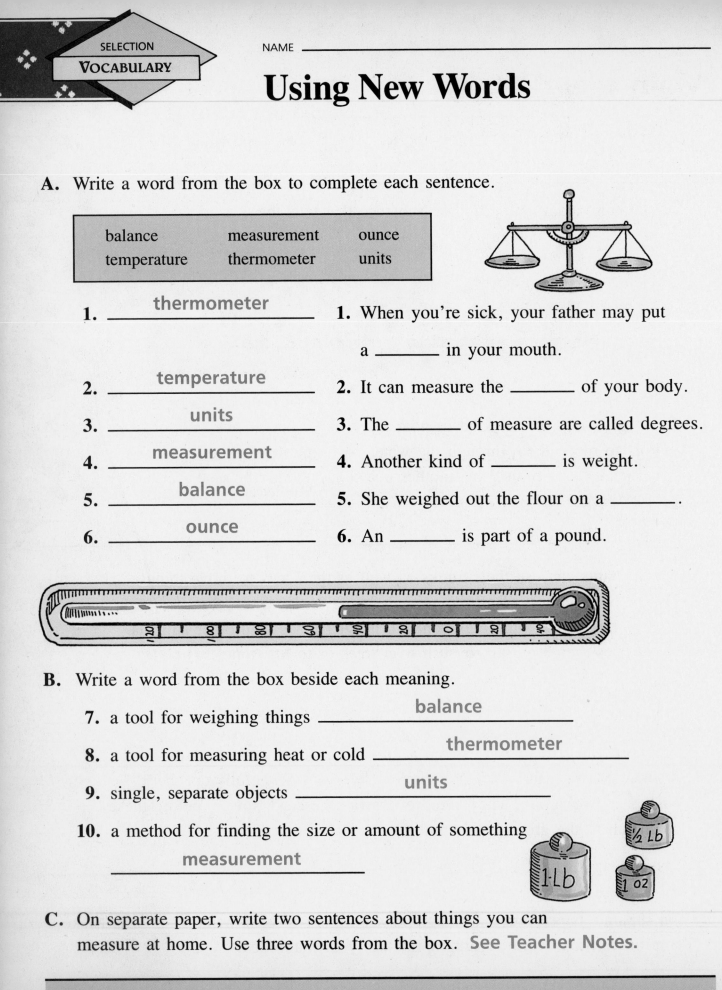

1. __thermometer__   1. When you're sick, your father may put

a _____ in your mouth.

2. __temperature__   2. It can measure the _____ of your body.

3. __units__   3. The _____ of measure are called degrees.

4. __measurement__   4. Another kind of _____ is weight.

5. __balance__   5. She weighed out the flour on a _____.

6. __ounce__   6. An _____ is part of a pound.

B. Write a word from the box beside each meaning.

7. a tool for weighing things ____balance____

8. a tool for measuring heat or cold ____thermometer____

9. single, separate objects ____units____

10. a method for finding the size or amount of something

____measurement____

C. On separate paper, write two sentences about things you can
measure at home. Use three words from the box. See Teacher Notes.

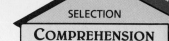

The Ins and Outs of Measurement

A. Complete the summary of the selection "The Ins and Outs of Measurement." **Accept reasonable variations.**

This selection is about different ways to ___**measure**___ things. People need to measure things because things come in ___**different**___ sizes.

A construction worker uses measurement to build ___**houses**___ . A scientist uses measurement to learn about nature. Most important, all people use measurement in their ___**daily**___ lives. Because things are measured in different ways, it is important to know many kinds of measurement.

One way people measure things is by weight. Weight is the pull of ___**the earth**___ on objects near its surface. Tools that measure weight are called balances or ___**scales**___ . Long ago people used handy objects like grain to measure weight. They didn't weigh things exactly. So people decided to use ___**standard**___ units of weights. In the English system, two standard units are ounces and ___**pounds**___ .

Scientists use many measuring tools. You don't have to be a scientist to invent ways to measure things. You can make a balance out of a ___**yardstick**___ and some string. You can also use a soup can and a ___**ruler**___ to measure how much rain falls during a storm. When you begin to think of your own ways to measure things, you are thinking like a scientist.

B. On separate paper, write three sentences that tell another way you could measure how much rain falls. **See Teacher Notes.**

Test-Taking

> **REMEMBER:** To do well on a test, prepare well, read directions carefully, and look over the test before beginning.

A. Read the sample test in the box. Then answer the questions below it. Do not take the sample test.

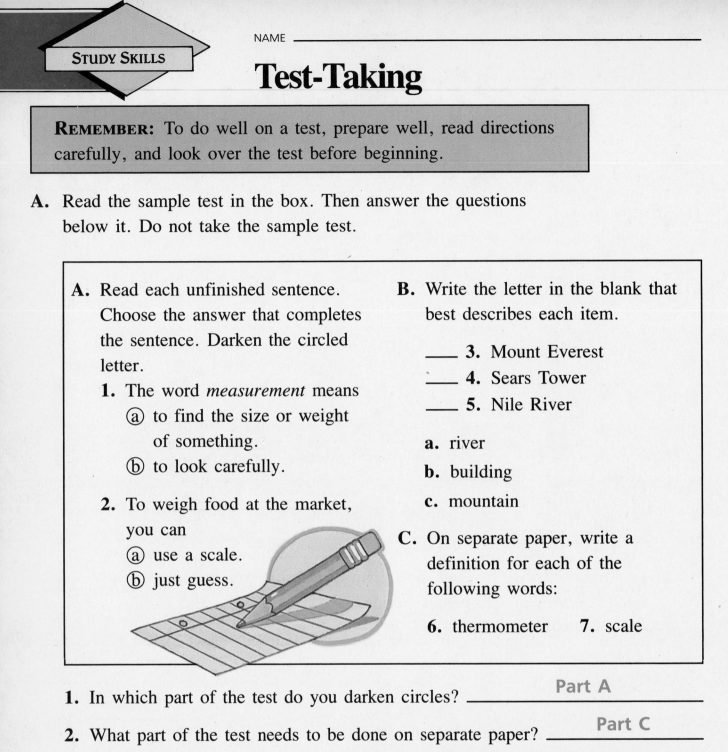

> **A.** Read each unfinished sentence. Choose the answer that completes the sentence. Darken the circled letter.
>
> 1. The word *measurement* means
>   ⓐ to find the size or weight of something.
>   ⓑ to look carefully.
>
> 2. To weigh food at the market, you can
>   ⓐ use a scale.
>   ⓑ just guess.
>
> **B.** Write the letter in the blank that best describes each item.
>
> ____ **3.** Mount Everest
> ____ **4.** Sears Tower
> ____ **5.** Nile River
>
> **a.** river
> **b.** building
> **c.** mountain
>
> **C.** On separate paper, write a definition for each of the following words:
>
> **6.** thermometer   **7.** scale

1. In which part of the test do you darken circles? _____ Part A _____

2. What part of the test needs to be done on separate paper? _____ Part C _____

3. What will you do in Part C? _____ Write a definition for each word. _____

4. In which part are you completing an unfinished sentence? _____ Part A _____

5. Which part of the test would probably take the longest? _____ Part C _____

B. On separate paper, write a short test with directions and two questions. **See Teacher Notes.**

Graphs

> **REMEMBER:** A **graph** is a drawing used to present numerical information. Use the caption, key, and labels to help you understand information on graphs.

A. Use the bar graph to help you answer the questions.

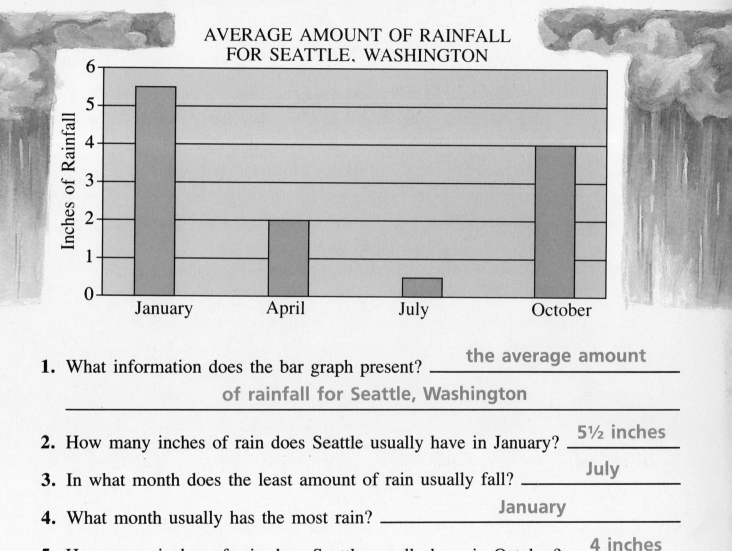

AVERAGE AMOUNT OF RAINFALL
FOR SEATTLE, WASHINGTON

1. What information does the bar graph present? __the average amount__
   __of rainfall for Seattle, Washington__

2. How many inches of rain does Seattle usually have in January? __5½ inches__

3. In what month does the least amount of rain usually fall? __July__

4. What month usually has the most rain? __January__

5. How many inches of rain does Seattle usually have in October? __4 inches__

6. What month has twice as much rain as the month of April? __October__

B. On separate paper, make a bar graph of information about the number of students in your school. Show the number of students in three or four different classes. **See Teacher Notes.**

Checkpoint

Read the paragraphs. Then fill in the circle beside the correct answer.

Chang loved birds. He liked to hear them sing outside his window in the morning. He liked to watch them as they flew. His room was covered with pictures of birds. Even his books were mostly about birds.

One day, Chang and his father made a feeder for the birds. They put it in a tree in Chang's yard and kept it filled with seeds. Every day Chang watched the birds and listened to them sing when they came to eat. Then one day the birds did not appear. Chang was puzzled. Then he noticed that a cat had climbed the tree and was waiting near the feeder. Chang told his father about the problem. His father got a saw, a hammer, some wood, and a rope. He took them outside and went to get some bolts, nails, screws, and glue.

With these things Chang and his father made a new feeder. This one was even nicer than the first one. When it was finished, they used the rope to hang it far out on the highest branch of the tree. Soon Chang was able to enjoy his wild friends as they came to the feeder. The cat also came back, but it was not able to bother the birds in the new feeder. As a result, the birds were not frightened away.

drawing conclusions

1. What caused the birds to come to the feeder every day?

(a) It always had plenty of seeds.

(b) It was in a tree.

(c) Chang watched them.

(d) Chang had made it for them.

drawing conclusions

2. Which words from the story helped you choose your answer?

(a) Chang loved birds.

(b) kept it filled with seeds

(c) put it in a tree

(d) listened to them sing

drawing conclusions

3. What happened because the cat waited near the feeder?

(a) The birds chased the cat.

(b) The birds were scared away.

(c) The birds ate more seeds.

(d) Chang fed the cat.

drawing conclusions

4. Which words from the story helped you choose your answer?

(a) near the feeder

(b) one day

(c) then he noticed

(d) birds did not appear

classification

5. <u>Hammer</u>, <u>saw</u>, <u>wood</u>, and <u>rope</u> are the names of _____ .

(a) things used for building

(b) things used for planting

(c) things used for cooking

(d) things used for feeding birds

classification

6. <u>Bolts</u>, <u>nails</u>, <u>screws</u>, and <u>glue</u> are all things you would buy in a _____ .

(a) toy store

(b) clothing store

(c) food store

(d) hardware store

drawing conclusions

7. Why was the cat unable to bother the birds in the new feeder?

(a) The cat could not reach it.

(b) The cat was afraid of it.

(c) The cat did not like it.

(d) The cat could not see it.

drawing conclusions

8. Which words from the story helped you choose your answer to 7?

(a) enjoy his wild friends

(b) the birds were not frightened

(c) far out on the highest branch

(d) even nicer than the first

NAME _____

Context Clues

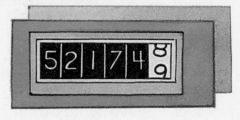

> **REMEMBER:** The words and sentences around an unknown word can help you figure out the meaning of that unknown word.

A. Read the sentences. Use the clues to figure out the meaning of each underlined word. Write the meaning.

1. The scientist sat at her desk and <u>calculated</u>, or figured out, how far the ship would travel.

   Calculated means _____**figured out**_____ .

2. Scientists get many bits of information when they measure things. They study these <u>data</u> for possible later use.

   Data means _____**bits of information**_____ .

3. The traveler looked at the <u>odometer</u> in his car when he wanted to know exactly how far he had driven that day.

   Odometer means __**an instrument showing the number of miles driven**__ .

4. When the captain started to feel hungry, he looked at the <u>chronometer</u> on the wall. He saw that it was already 12:30 P.M.

   Chronometer means _____**clock**_____ .

5. <u>Weight</u>, or the pull of the earth on objects near its surface, is measured with a scale or balance.

   Weight means _____**the pull of earth on objects**_____ .

6. The weather forecaster predicted a storm because his <u>barometer</u> showed that air pressure was falling.

   Barometer means _____**an instrument measuring air pressure**_____ .

B. Make up three new words. On separate paper, use these words in sentences that will help someone else figure out what they mean. **See Teacher Notes.**

Using New Words

A. Match each word or words with the synonyms from the box.
Write the synonym on the line.

bridge	instrument	melody

1. tune _____ melody _____

2. violin part _____ bridge _____

3. music maker _____ instrument _____

B. Read the following sentences. Then use each of the words and
its synonym from Part A to complete the sentences below.

4. My brother Ted plays an _____ instrument _____ and practices every

day on his _____ music maker _____ .

5. Once while Ted practiced, the _____ bridge _____ of his violin

broke, and he had to wait several weeks to get a new

_____ violin part _____ .

6. Ted just learned a new _____ melody _____ from his teacher, and

I can't get the lovely _____ tune _____ out of my head.

C. Think of another meaning for the story words *bridge* and
instrument. On separate paper, write a sentence using each new
meaning. See Teacher Notes.

Fidelia

A. Complete the summary of the story "Fidelia."

Accept reasonable variations.

This is the story of a girl named _____Fidelia_____ . Most of

the story takes place in Miss Toomey's _____band room_____ .

Fidelia Ortega didn't play a musical instrument. One day she decided

she wanted to learn how to play the _____violin_____ . But

everyone told her to _____wait_____ until she grew a little more.

One day Fidelia sneaked into the band room. Suddenly, there was a
crash as Fidelia tripped over the drums. When Miss Toomey, the
conductor, asked Fidelia what she was doing, Fidelia told her about her
wish to play the violin. Miss Toomey told her she was too

_____small_____ . "How about playing the _____tom-tom_____ ?"
she asked. And that was how Fidelia joined the orchestra.

Fidelia was happy to be in the orchestra, but she still wanted to play
the violin. She heard Mrs. Reed, director of the

_____All City Orchestra_____ , was coming to choose
the school's best players. Fidelia had a plan. She made her own violin

out of a box, some wood, and _____rubber bands_____ for strings.
Finally the day for All City Orchestra tryouts came. Suddenly everyone
heard a strange sound from the back of the orchestra. It was Fidelia

playing her _____homemade violin_____ .

Mrs. Reed saw how hard Fidelia was trying. "Do you want to play

a _____real_____ violin, Fidelia?" asked Mrs. Reed. Mrs. Reed opened
a tiny case and handed Fidelia a beautiful little violin. That's how Fidelia
started to learn to play the violin.

B. Imagine a year has gone by and Fidelia is about to play her
violin for the All City Orchestra tryouts. On separate paper,
write about what happens. See Teacher Notes.

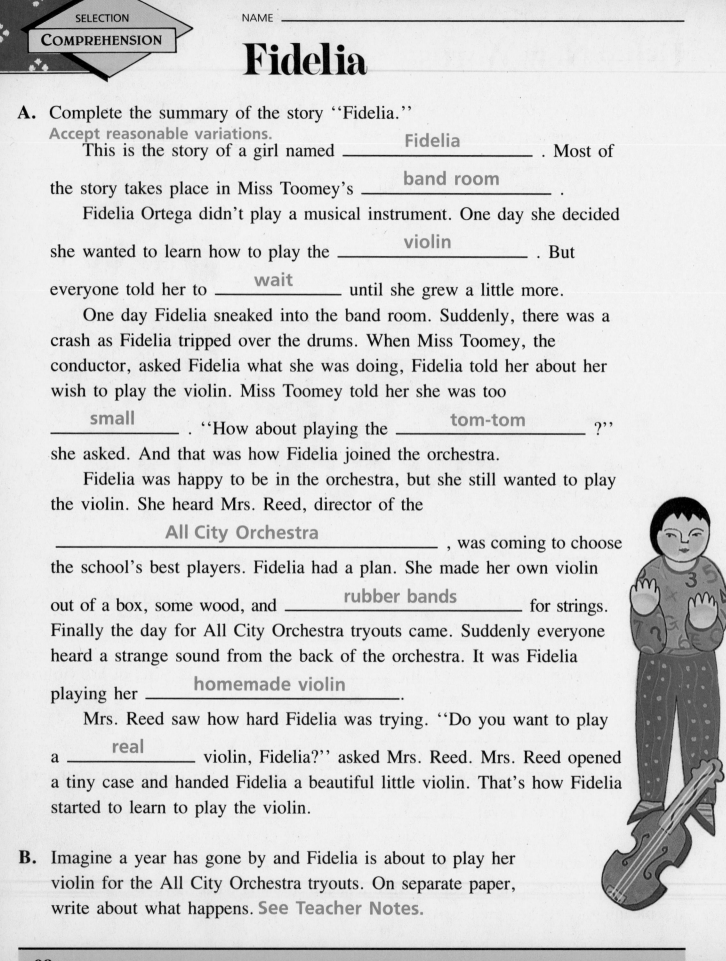

Graphs

> **REMEMBER:** A **graph** is a drawing used to present numerical information. Use the caption, key, and labels to help you understand information on graphs.

A. Read the two bar graphs below. Then answer the questions.

Players in the All-City Orchestra

Clarinets
Drums
Trombones
Violins

0 1 2 3 4 5 6 7 8 9

Concerts Given by the All City Orchestra

5
4
3
2
1
0

Sept.   Oct.   Nov.   Dec.

1. What does the first graph show? _It shows what instruments are played in the All City Orchestra and how many people play each one._

2. What does the second graph show? _It shows how many concerts the orchestra gave in September, October, November, and December._

3. Which instrument is played by the most players in the All City Orchestra? _The violin has the most players._

4. In what month did the orchestra give the fewest concerts? _September_

5. How many trombone players are there in the orchestra? _four_

B. Count the total number of boys and girls in your class. On separate paper, make a bar graph comparing the numbers. _See Teacher Notes._

COMPREHENSION

Drawing Conclusions

> **REMEMBER:** When you **draw a conclusion,** you figure out things that are not explained in a story. Use story clues and what you already know to draw a conclusion.

A. Read each paragraph. Draw a conclusion. Write a sentence to answer each question.

1.   Fidelia has just finished second grade. Her favorite subject is music. During the summer she plans to read a book about the history of music. When school starts in the fall, Fidelia wants to take music lessons.

What grade will Fidelia be in in the fall? Fidelia will be in third grade.

2.   Miss Toomey passed out new song books to her class. She wrote a page number on the board and asked her students to turn to that page. Next she asked them to listen while she played the song on that page. Then she asked them to stand with their books open to the new song.

What do you think Miss Toomey finally asked her class to do? _____
Miss Toomey asked her class to sing the new song.

3.   Bill found an old box. He cut a hole in its center. Bill then added a piece of wood to one end of the box and another small piece of wood for the bridge. He stretched rubber bands over the box for strings and attached a shoulder strap.

What kind of a homemade instrument did Bill make? Bill made
a homemade guitar.

B. To walk to school, Paul plans to wear a heavy jacket, some gloves, a wool hat, and a scarf. On separate paper, write a sentence that draws a conclusion about the weather for Paul's walk to school. See Teacher Notes.

Using New Words

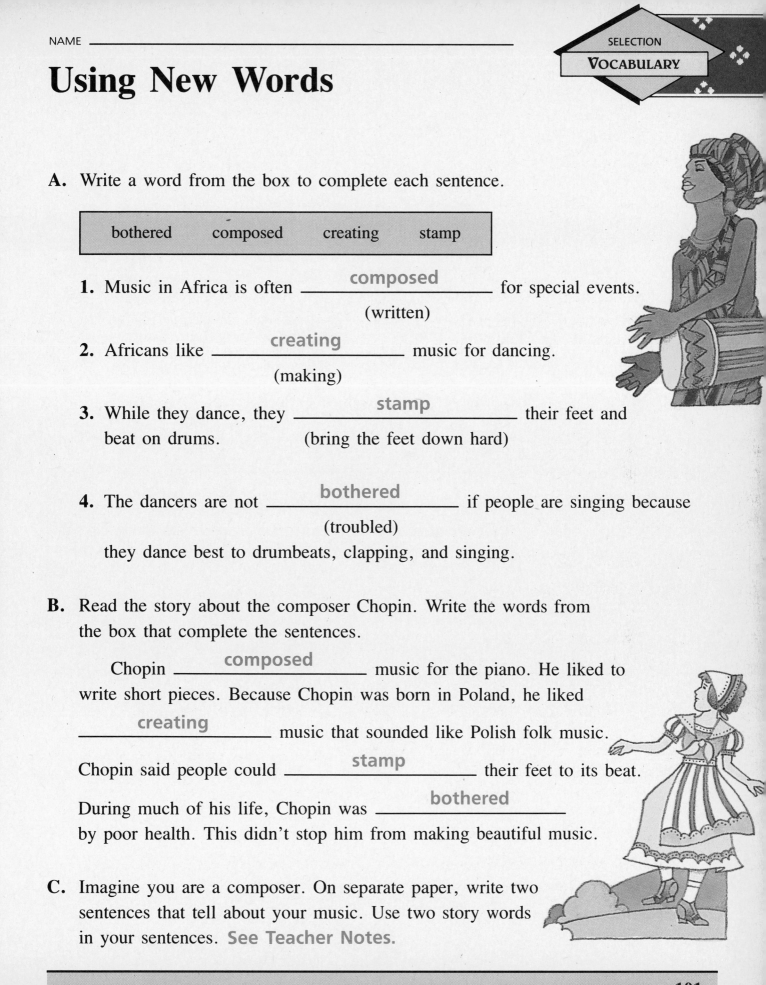

A. Write a word from the box to complete each sentence.

| bothered | composed | creating | stamp |

1. Music in Africa is often ___*composed*___ for special events.
   (written)

2. Africans like ___*creating*___ music for dancing.
   (making)

3. While they dance, they ___*stamp*___ their feet and beat on drums. (bring the feet down hard)

4. The dancers are not ___*bothered*___ if people are singing because
   (troubled)
   they dance best to drumbeats, clapping, and singing.

B. Read the story about the composer Chopin. Write the words from the box that complete the sentences.

Chopin ___*composed*___ music for the piano. He liked to write short pieces. Because Chopin was born in Poland, he liked ___*creating*___ music that sounded like Polish folk music.

Chopin said people could ___*stamp*___ their feet to its beat.

During much of his life, Chopin was ___*bothered*___ by poor health. This didn't stop him from making beautiful music.

C. Imagine you are a composer. On separate paper, write two sentences that tell about your music. Use two story words in your sentences. **See Teacher Notes.**

Ludwig van Beethoven: Master of a Silent World

A. Complete the summary of the selection "Ludwig van Beethoven: Master of a Silent World." Accept reasonable variations.

This is a selection about ___Ludwig van___

___Beethoven___ , a famous musician who couldn't hear.

Much of the story happens in ___Vienna___ , Austria, where Beethoven lived and wrote.

Beethoven grew up in a musical family. His father began giving

him ___piano___ lessons when he was just four. After his mother died, Ludwig supported his family by playing

___piano concerts___ .

In addition to playing music, Beethoven ___wrote/created music___ . It took him a long time to write each piece because he wanted each note to be perfect and beautiful.

When Beethoven turned twenty-eight, he began to lose

___his hearing___ . He went to doctors, but they could do nothing. Beethoven didn't want his friends to know he was going deaf so he stopped going out much. Still, he loved to write music. Even though

he couldn't hear anything, Beethoven kept ___writing it___ .

By 1819, Beethoven was totally ___deaf___ , but his music was more beautiful than ever. He couldn't hear with his ears so he

listened instead with his ___mind___ and his ___heart___ .

B. Imagine you are Beethoven and are deaf. On separate paper, write two sentences that tell someone about a piece you have written. See Teacher Notes.

Classification

> **REMEMBER:** To **classify** words, decide how they are alike and different in meaning.

A. Read each group of words. Write a word from the box that will fit each group.

baseball	bicycle	drums
green	lemon	mouth

1. violins   trumpets   trombones   pianos   1. _drums_

2. pink   yellow   red   brown   2. _green_

3. tennis   football   soccer   basketball   3. _baseball_

4. ears   eyes   nose   teeth   4. _mouth_

5. bus   train   airplane   car   5. _bicycle_

6. orange   apple   banana   grape   6. _lemon_

B. Write the words from the box that belong under each group.

clarinet	flute	hammer
harp	nails	wood

7. Instruments People Play

clarinet

flute

harp

8. Things for Buildings

hammer

nails

wood

C. On separate paper, write the titles Songs I Like and Songs I Dislike. Then write three examples for each group. See Teacher Notes.

NAME

Comparison

> **REMEMBER: Comparisons** tell how things, people, or events are alike and different. Signal words and story clues help you understand comparisons.

A. Read the paragraph. Complete the chart. Use a — for no and a + for yes.

    A piano and a violin are both similar and different. They both have strings. A violin has four strings. You can easily see a violin's strings. The musician uses a bow to play them. A piano usually has 88 strings. However, the strings in a piano are often hidden. The musician pushes the keys to play them. Both instruments can make beautiful music.

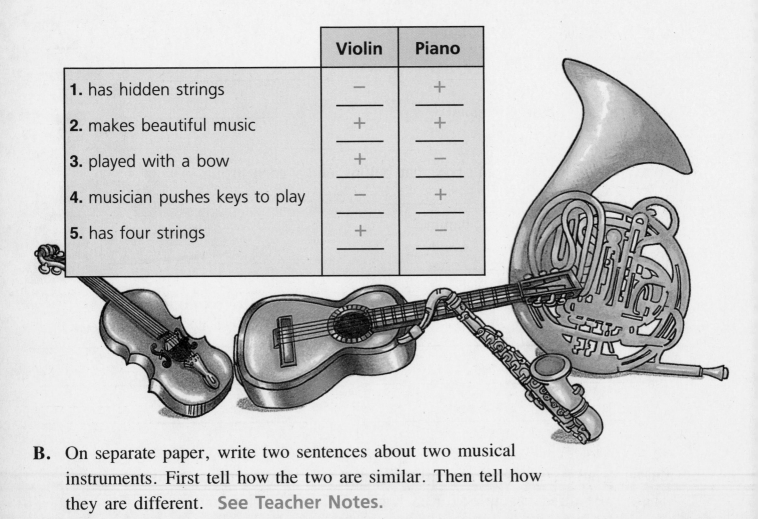

	Violin	Piano
1. has hidden strings	−	+
2. makes beautiful music	+	+
3. played with a bow	+	−
4. musician pushes keys to play	−	+
5. has four strings	+	−

B. On separate paper, write two sentences about two musical instruments. First tell how the two are similar. Then tell how they are different. **See Teacher Notes.**

Using New Words

A. Read the story. Write the missing words.

assistant	bandage	bicuspid	formula	patients

John was the doctor's _____assistant_____ . He helped the

doctor with all of her _____patients_____ . When a patient had

a cut or sore paw, John put a _____bandage_____ over the cut

to keep out the dirt. Sometimes the parents were not sure what milk

_____formula_____ to use for their babies. John would help.

He would write down what the doctor said was best. The one problem

John didn't help with was sore teeth. If someone called with a

sore _____bicuspid_____ , John would tell him to call a dentist!

B. Read each sentence. Choose a word from the box that means
almost the same thing as the underlined word or words. Then
write each sentence with the word you chose.

1. If you cut a finger, you should cover it with a <u>strip of cloth used to cover
a cut</u>. _If you cut a finger, you should cover it with a bandage._

2. If you are <u>an aide or helper to someone</u>, you should follow her directions
carefully. _If you are an assistant to someone, you should follow
her directions carefully._

C. Imagine you are someone's assistant. On separate paper, write
two sentences that tell about what you do. Use at least two story
words. See Teacher Notes.

Doctor De Soto

A. Complete the summary of the story "Doctor De Soto."
Accept reasonable variations.

This story is about _____ Doctor De Soto _____,

his assistant and one of their patients, _____ a fox _____.

The story takes place in Doctor De Soto's _____ office _____.

Doctor De Soto was a good dentist. Because he was a mouse, big animals liked him. He could get right inside their mouths to work. But

he and his assistant, who also happened to be _____ his wife _____,

had one rule. They would not treat animals who were

_____ dangerous _____ to mice. One day they looked out their

window and saw a fox who was crying. They both knew that foxes like to eat mice.

Finally, they let the fox in. The doctor said he would have to

_____ pull _____ the rotten tooth. He gave the fox some _____ gas _____

so he wouldn't feel the pain. The fox talked about wanting to eat Doctor De Soto and his wife. After the fox left, Doctor De Soto and his wife talked. How could they finish their job and not get eaten by the fox?

The next day the fox came for his new tooth. He also had plans

to _____ eat _____ the mice. After the tooth was in place, Doctor De

Soto told the fox about a new treatment to get rid of

_____ toothaches _____ forever. Doctor De Soto painted each

tooth with a secret formula. Then he told the fox to shut his mouth. The

formula was really _____ glue _____. The fox couldn't get his mouth

open for anything! That is how Doctor De Soto and his assistant finished their job without being finished themselves.

B. On separate paper, write about another adventure Doctor De Soto might have with another patient. See Teacher Notes.

Drawing Conclusions

> **REMEMBER:** When you **draw a conclusion,** you figure out things that are not explained in a story. Use story clues and what you already know to draw a conclusion.

A. Read each new event. Then answer the questions.

1. Doctor De Soto and his assistant heard a knock on the door of their office. They looked out the window. It was a wolf. They knew that wolves weren't nice to mice. The wolf was smiling. He didn't seem to have a toothache.

a. How do Doctor De Soto and his assistant feel? Possible response: They are nervous and a little afraid.

b. How do you know this? Possible response: They know wolves aren't nice to mice. The wolf doesn't seem to have a toothache.

2. A pig rang the bell. Doctor De Soto looked through the window. He could see the pig holding her mouth so he opened the door.
"Let me look in your mouth," said Doctor De Soto.
The pig opened her mouth and cried.
"We will have to take this one," said Doctor De Soto.

a. What is Doctor De Soto referring to? Possible response: He is talking about a tooth he will have to pull.

b. How do you know this? Possible response: He is looking in the pig's mouth. He knows the tooth is bad.

B. From what you already know, decide whether a robin or a wolf might be afraid of the fox. On separate paper, write a sentence that tells what helped you decide. See Teacher Notes.

Checkpoint

Read the graphs. Then fill in the circle beside the correct answer. Chang made a graph to show how many birds he saw at his feeder each day for five days. Use Graph A to answer questions 1-4.

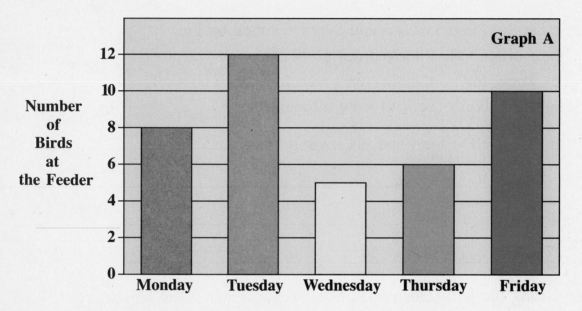

Chang made another graph to show how many ounces of seed the birds ate each month during the winter. Use Graph B to answer questions 5-8.

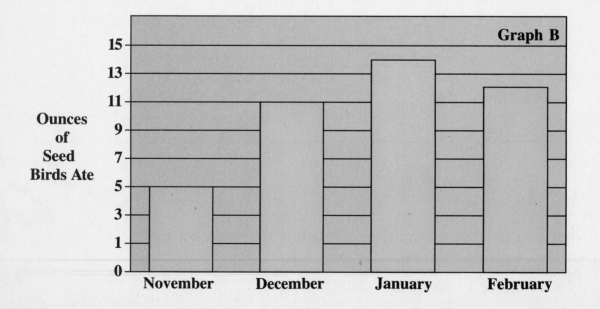

Checkpoint

graphs

1. How many birds did Chang see at the feeder on Monday?
   (a) 4
   (b) 6
   (c) 8
   (d) 10

graphs

2. Chang saw the fewest number of birds at the feeder on _____ .
   (a) Monday
   (b) Tuesday
   (c) Wednesday
   (d) Thursday

graphs

3. Chang saw the greatest number of birds at the feeder on _____ .
   (a) Monday
   (b) Tuesday
   (c) Wednesday
   (d) Friday

graphs

4. How many birds did Chang see at the feeder on Wednesday?
   (a) 4
   (b) 5
   (c) 6
   (d) 7

graphs

5. During which month did the birds eat the most seed?
   (a) November
   (b) December
   (c) January
   (d) February

graphs

6. How much seed did the birds eat during February?
   (a) 11 ounces
   (b) 12 ounces
   (c) 13 ounces
   (d) 14 ounces

graphs

7. How much seed did the birds eat during January?
   (a) 12 ounces
   (b) 13 ounces
   (c) 14 ounces
   (d) 15 ounces

graphs

8. During which month did the birds eat the least seed?
   (a) November
   (b) December
   (c) January
   (d) February

Vocabulary Review

Fill in the circle beside the word that best fits in the sentence.

1. A long time ago, poor farmers were called _____ .
   a) courtiers
   b) advisers
   c) redcoats
   d) peasants

2. A doctor's _____ helps the doctor with patients.
   a) bandage
   b) bicuspid
   c) assistant
   d) prince

3. You can tell if two things weigh the same if you use a _____ .
   a) measurement
   b) bridge
   c) formula
   d) balance

4. If you don't know the words to the song, just hum the _____ .
   a) instrument
   b) alarm
   c) formula
   d) melody

5. The British soldiers who fought in the American War for Independence were called _____ because of the color of their coats.
   a) colonists
   b) hoofbeats
   c) advisers
   d) redcoats

6. Giant pieces of stone were loaded on the large, flat _____ , which moved them across the bay.
   a) barge
   b) prince
   c) herald
   d) balance

7. Just as the train was due to leave, the conductor _____ the people that they could not start for ten minutes.
   a) bothered
   b) informed
   c) composed
   d) assigned

8. My dentist uses a _____ to make fillings, which she mixes using special directions.

    a) pattern

    b) formula

    c) thermometer

    d) conservatory

9. With some music it is fun to _____ out the beat with your feet.

    a) alert

    b) bind

    c) identify

    d) stamp

10. Beethoven _____ much music after he could no longer hear.

    a) composed

    b) informed

    c) realized

    d) bothered

11. Fidelia wanted to play a musical _____ so badly that she made a violin.

    a) melody

    b) measurement

    c) formula

    d) instrument

12. When David scraped his knee, he put a _____ over the sore.

    a) bandage

    b) formula

    c) barge

    d) thermometer

13. Ludwig van Beethoven is well known for _____ music that is powerful and joyful.

    a) picnicking

    b) creating

    c) considering

    d) boring

14. The warning of the fire _____ could be heard loudly.

    a) alarm

    b) units

    c) barge

    d) herald

15. Many of the _____ who had come from England to settle in Boston thought the tax on tea was unfair.

    a) colonists

    b) redcoats

    c) advisers

    d) patients

 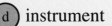

Unit Wrap-Up

NAME _____

Read each question. Write your answer, using complete sentences.

1. In "The Ins and Outs of Measurement," you read about the way scientists deal with problems. How did P'ei in "8,000 Stones" act like a scientist when he solved the problem of how to weigh the elephant? **Possible response: He saw something happen and looked for a reason. Then he explained to others what he knew about weighing the elephant.**

2. In "Fidelia," everyone told Fidelia that she was too young to play in the orchestra. Do you think Beethoven would have told Fidelia the same thing? Why or why not? **Possible response: Since Beethoven learned to play the piano when he was four, he probably would not have thought Fidelia was too young. He also knew that it was important to overcome problems if you loved to do something.**

3. Both Sybil in "Sybil Rides by Night" and Doctor De Soto in "Doctor De Soto" showed courage. Who do you think was braver? Explain your choice. **Possible response: Students should explore the dangers the characters faced and the way they dealt with their fears.**

Interest Inventory

Weather can make a difference in people and animals. What interests you about weather? Answer the questions below and use the chart to discover books that you may find especially interesting.

yes no

1. ☐ ☐ Do you like learning about nature?
2. ☐ ☐ Do you like to watch the sky at night?
3. ☐ ☐ Are things found in nature useful?
4. ☐ ☐ Would you like to read a story about animals?
5. ☐ ☐ Do you like finding out about the world around you?
6. ☐ ☐ Have you ever planted things and watched them grow?
7. ☐ ☐ Do you like learning about different kinds of weather?

Now find the numbers for the questions you checked YES. Follow the column down. When you see a star, move across the row to find the book title. That's the book for you!

1	2	3	4	5	6	7	Title/Author
★	★			★			*The Moon Seems to Change* by Franklyn M. Branley
★	★	★	★	★		★	*Three Days on a River in a Red Canoe* by Vera B. Williams
	★					★	*A Walk on a Snowy Night* by Judy Delton
★		★		★	★	★	*The Seasons* by David Lambert
		★	★				*The Wump World* by Bill Peet
			★	★			*Why Mosquitos Buzz in People's Ears* by Verna Aardema
★		★		★			*Snips & Snails & Walnut Whales* by Phyllis Fiarotta

Personal Book List

NAME _____

Title _____

Author _____

Title _____

Author _____

Title _____

Author _____

Title _____

Author _____

Story Elements

> **REMEMBER:** To help you understand stories, look for clues and details that tell about the setting of a story.

A. Read each sentence about the story and the words that follow it. Circle the words that complete each sentence. Then write them on the line.

1. This story took place _____ long ago _____ .

   (long ago)   about 25 years ago   very recently

2. Captains then learned the depth of the sea from

   _____ plumb lines _____ .

   charts   (plumb lines)   sonar equipment

3. This story was set _____ in the Atlantic Ocean _____ .

   on the Mississippi River   (in the Atlantic Ocean)   on Lake Erie

4. The nearest land was _____ Cape Cod _____ .

   Hawaii   (Cape Cod)   England

5. The *Courser* was _____ a large sailboat _____ .

   a rowboat   an ocean liner   (a large sailboat)

6. The weather at the beginning of the story was

   _____ wild and windy _____ .

   warm and sunny   cold and snowy   (wild and windy)

7. What a sailor could see in front of him during the storm was

   _____ barely anything _____ .

   (barely anything)   mountains in the distance   children on the beach

B. On separate paper, describe the setting for a story about a blizzard. **See Teacher Notes.**

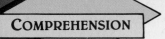

COMPREHENSION

Cause/Effect

> **REMEMBER:** Use signal words, story clues, and what you already know to figure out which events caused other events to happen.

A. Read the paragraph. Write the missing causes or effects.

Yesterday's heavy snowstorm caused many problems. At first, roads were slippery. This caused several cars to crash. Later, the snow became so thick that drivers had to stop because they couldn't see. When the roads were blocked, schools were closed. The wet snow was so heavy that many trees fell over. Some trees fell on telephone wires. As a result, telephones were not working in some places.

1. Cause: Roads were slippery.

   Effect: Several cars crashed.

2. Cause: The snow was so thick, drivers couldn't see.

   Effect: Drivers had to stop.

3. Cause: The roads were blocked.

   Effect: Schools were closed.

4. Cause: The snow was very heavy.

   Effect: Many trees fell over.

5. Cause: Trees fell on telephone wires.

   Effect: Telephones were not working in some places.

B. Imagine a snowstorm blocked all the streets of your town. On separate paper, write sentences that tell at least three effects this would have on your family. See Teacher Notes.

Using New Words

A. Write the word from the box that matches each meaning.

boasted	contest	gust	hurricane	tremendous

1. _____gust_____ sudden rush of air

2. _____contest_____ game in which there is a winner

3. _____boasted_____ bragged

4. _____tremendous_____ very large

5. _____hurricane_____ very strong wind storm

B. Read the paragraph. Use words from the box to complete the sentences.

My aunt likes to sail in races. Once she won a sailing _____contest_____ because of the weather. Another sailor had _____boasted_____ that he was better than my aunt. They decided to have a race. It was almost a tie, but near the end of the race my aunt took down most of her sails because the sky had grown dark. Just then, a _____tremendous_____ storm hit. The wind howled. The storm was almost as bad as a _____hurricane_____ . One huge _____gust_____ of wind tore the sails off the other boat, and my aunt won. She says a good sailor always watches the weather.

C. Imagine that a big storm is coming. On separate paper, tell what you would do to get ready for it. Use at least three words from the box. **See Teacher Notes.**

The Wind and the Sun

A. Complete the summary of the story "The Wind and the Sun."
Accept reasonable variations.

This is a story about the _____Wind_____ and the _____Sun_____ .

It takes place one _____morning_____ just after Sun had gotten up.

Sun smiled to herself. Suddenly, she felt a whoosh of air. It was Wind. Wind had blown a cloud right over Sun's face. Sun and Wind talked about how strong each of them was. Sun said she was stronger because she could make the flowers bloom. Wind said she was stronger because she could blow the _____petals_____ right off the flowers. Both thought they were stronger. Then Sun had an idea. They would have a _____contest_____ . They would decide who was stronger. Sun looked down and saw a man on the road. "See that man," said Sun. "Let's see who can make him take off his _____cape_____ ."

Wind went first. She blew and blew. Everything shook, and windows rattled. But the harder Wind blew, the _____colder_____ the man got and the tighter he held on to his cape. Wind got too tired to blow any longer.

Then it was Sun's turn. Sun turned her face toward earth and smiled. The man got warmer, and soon he undid the buttons on his cape. When he got too hot, he _____took off the cape_____ . He was glad to take it off.

"See," said Sun. "Now tell me which of us is stronger." Wind knew the answer. Sun was the _____stronger_____ .

The lesson you can learn is that you can do more with _____gentleness_____ than with force.

B. Think of another story that tells the same lesson. Write your story on separate paper. See Teacher Notes.

Dictionary

REMEMBER: You use a **dictionary** to learn the spelling, pronunciation, meaning, and origin of words.

A. Read the pairs of dictionary guide words. Write the word from the box that would be on the same page as the guide words. The first one is done for you.

cloud	frozen	rain	snow	storm	winter

1. stick-stuck ___storm___

2. clear-cluck ___cloud___

3. west-work ___winter___

4. snap-soak ___snow___

5. rack-rest ___rain___

6. frog-fruit ___frozen___

B. Write a word from the box next to the dictionary respelling that shows how to say the word.

freeze	hail	ice	rain	sleet	snow

7. īs ___ice___

8. frēz ___freeze___

9. snō ___snow___

10. rān ___rain___

11. slēt ___sleet___

12. hāl ___hail___

C. On separate paper, write the words from both boxes in alphabetical order. See Teacher Notes.

Cause/Effect

> **REMEMBER:** Use signal words, story clues, and what you already know to figure out which events caused other events to happen.

A. Read the paragraph. Then write the answers to the questions.

Sun wanted to smile but Cloud was in the way. As a result, when Cloud went away, Sun smiled so sweetly that all the flowers on the earth popped out of the ground. Then Wind let out a huge gust of air that caused trees to bend. The walking man held his cape more tightly because of the strong wind. When Sun shone, however, the man grew warm. Soon he became too warm, and he took off his cape.

1. Why did Sun smile? _Cloud went away._ _____

_____

2. What was the effect of Sun's smile on the flowers? _All the flowers_ _____
popped out of the ground. _____

3. What made the trees bend? _A huge gust of air made the trees bend._

_____

4. What effect did the strong wind have on the walking man? _He held his_ _____
cape more tightly. _____

5. What happened when the man became too warm? _He took off his cape._

_____

B. On separate paper, write a paragraph that tells what effects staying out in the hot sun for a long time might have on you.
See Teacher Notes.

Long Word Decoding

> **REMEMBER:** When you try to read a long word, look for words and word parts you know.

A. Circle the word part at the beginning or end of the words. Then write the uncircled words.

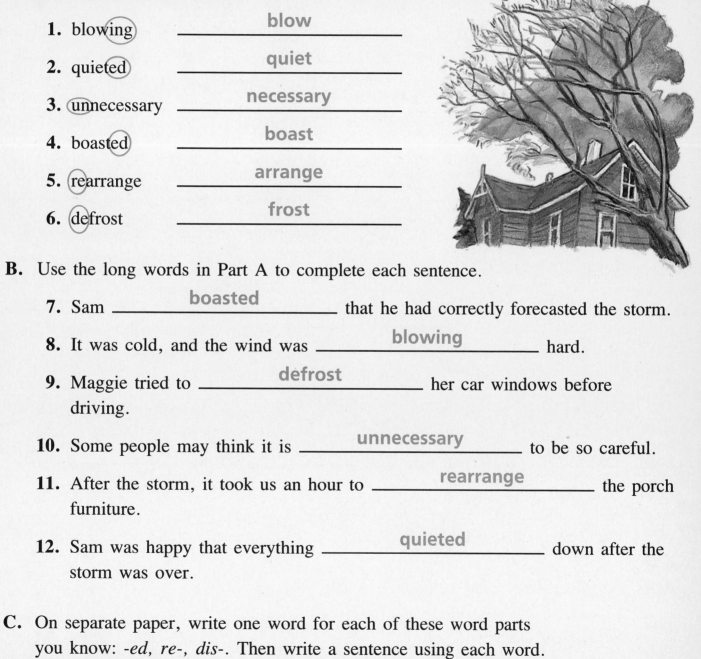

1. blow(ing) ___blow___

2. quiet(ed) ___quiet___

3. (un)necessary ___necessary___

4. boast(ed) ___boast___

5. (re)arrange ___arrange___

6. (de)frost ___frost___

B. Use the long words in Part A to complete each sentence.

7. Sam ___boasted___ that he had correctly forecasted the storm.

8. It was cold, and the wind was ___blowing___ hard.

9. Maggie tried to ___defrost___ her car windows before driving.

10. Some people may think it is ___unnecessary___ to be so careful.

11. After the storm, it took us an hour to ___rearrange___ the porch furniture.

12. Sam was happy that everything ___quieted___ down after the storm was over.

C. On separate paper, write one word for each of these word parts you know: *-ed, re-, dis-*. Then write a sentence using each word. **See Teacher Notes.**

NAME _____

Using New Words

A. Read each group of words. Write a word from the box that fits in the group.

atmosphere	droughts	evaluating	forecast
meteorologist	moisture	radar	

1. scientist   weatherperson   reporter _____ **meteorologist** _____

2. future   report   tomorrow _____ **forecast** _____

3. water   wet   drops _____ **moisture** _____

4. storms   floods   heat waves _____ **droughts** _____

5. sky   air   gases _____ **atmosphere** _____

6. waves   measure   radio _____ **radar** _____

7. studying   testing   judging _____ **evaluating** _____

B. Complete each sentence with a word from the box.

8. My father is a _____ **meteorologist** _____ who tells what the weather will be.

9. He can _____ **forecast** _____ the weather accurately.

10. When he's not giving the weather on TV, my dad is _____ **evaluating** _____ information he receives.

11. He measures the wind's speed and the amount of _____ **moisture** _____ in the air.

C. On separate paper, write a forecast for tomorrow's weather. Use two story words. **See Teacher Notes.**

AN INTERVIEW WITH A
Meteorologist

A. Complete the summary of "An Interview with a Meteorologist."
Accept reasonable variations.

This is about a boy named George and his interview with a

_____ meteorologist _____ , Mr. Dreumont. The

interview was part of a _____ science _____ project.

Mr. Dreumont grew up in Brownsville, Texas. In South Texas,

the weather often changes _____ very suddenly _____ .

Mr. Dreumont decided to become a meteorologist after he wrote a paper

on _____ hurricanes _____ . After working in Brownsville, he

went to several other places. Then he got a job in Boise, Idaho, where

he specializes in forecasting _____ forest fires _____ . During

dry thunderstorms, the _____ rain _____ evaporates before it gets to

the ground. The lightning bolts can start forest fires.

Because Mr. Dreumont speaks _____ Spanish _____ as well as

English, he has talked to other meteorologists in countries like Spain and

Chile. They talk about _____ problems in forecasting weather _____

and about new technology.

On a typical day of work, the first thing Mr. Dreumont does is use

the _____ computer _____ . Then he and his staff discuss the

information. They also use many special weather instruments for

information. The hardest things to forecast are big events like floods

and blizzards. Mr. Dreumont likes his job because _____

_____ the weather is different every day _____ .

B. On separate paper, write about a weather project you would like
to try. See Teacher Notes.

NAME _____

Long Word Decoding

> **REMEMBER:** When you try to read a long word, look for words and word parts you know.

A. Circle the word parts you know at the beginning and end of the words. Then write each word that is left uncircled.

1. (re)discover(ed)   _discover_____

2. discuss(ion)   _discuss_____

3. (re)construct(ion)   _construct_____

4. (re)check   _check_____

5. (un)twist(ed)   _twist_____

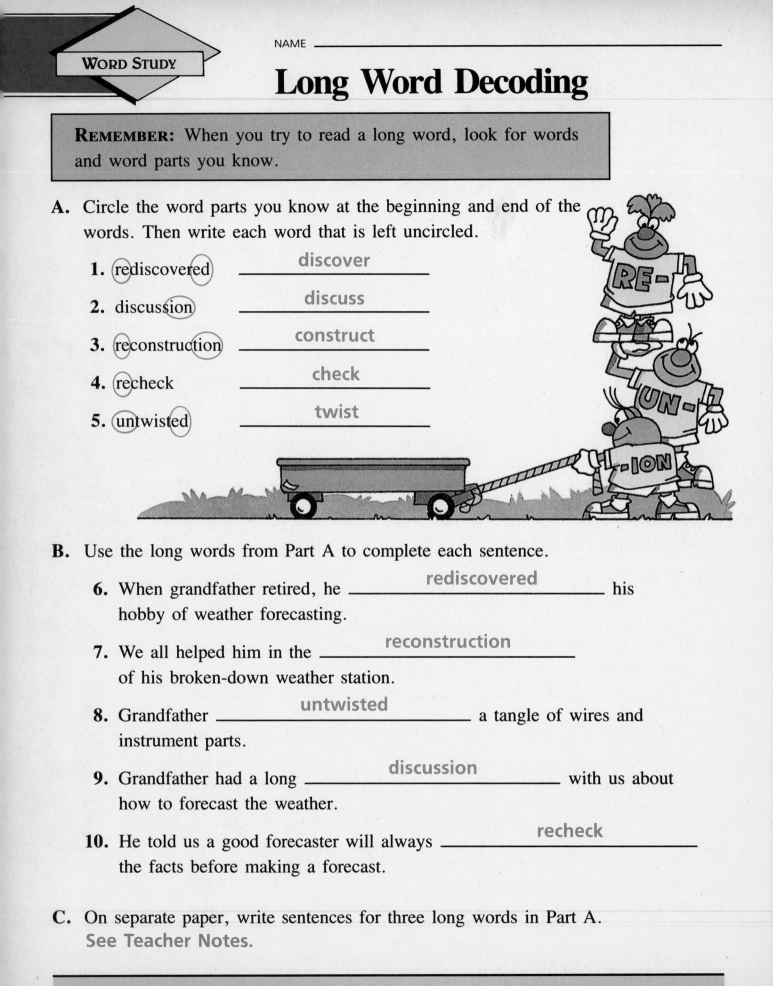

B. Use the long words from Part A to complete each sentence.

6. When grandfather retired, he ___rediscovered___ his hobby of weather forecasting.

7. We all helped him in the ___reconstruction___ of his broken-down weather station.

8. Grandfather ___untwisted___ a tangle of wires and instrument parts.

9. Grandfather had a long ___discussion___ with us about how to forecast the weather.

10. He told us a good forecaster will always ___recheck___ the facts before making a forecast.

C. On separate paper, write sentences for three long words in Part A.
   See Teacher Notes.

Dictionary

REMEMBER: You use a **dictionary** to learn the spelling, pronunciation, meaning, and origin of words.

A. Read the dictionary guide words. Write the two words from each group that would be on the same page.

1. **a.** doctor
   b. dirt
   c. decide
   d. detective

deer	distance
detective	
dirt	

2. **a.** mouse
   b. mine
   c. monkey
   d. middle

mile	mountain
mine	
monkey	

B. Look at the dictionary key words in the box. Then read each word below and its pronunciation. Write the key word on the line beside the word that uses the same vowel sound.

a	**a**sk	e	t**e**n	i	**i**s	o	h**o**t
ā	**a**pe	ē	m**ee**t	ī	**i**ce	ō	**o**pen

3. way (wā) _____ape_____

4. eye (ī) _____ice_____

5. add (ad) _____ask_____

6. rose (rōz) _____open_____

7. see (sē) _____meet_____

8. thread (thred) _____ten_____

C. On separate paper, make a chart that shows in which part of the dictionary you would find each word in Part B. Use the headings Beginning, Middle, and End. See Teacher Notes.

Checkpoint

Read the paragraphs. Then fill in the circle beside the correct answer.

On the day before the big snowstorm, Kim's mother bought a lot of groceries. She wanted to make sure there was plenty of food in the house. She told Kim that once before when a big storm came, she had almost run out of food. Because the snow had been so deep, she had not been able to drive to the store. This time she was taking no chances.

The next day, when Kim got up, she saw three feet of snow on the ground. Kim ran downstairs. Her father was still home. All the roads were closed. As a result, he couldn't go to work and Kim couldn't go to school. Kim was glad. She asked if they could all go to a movie. But her mother reminded her that they couldn't drive anywhere. Then Kim asked if she could call her best friend. Her father told her that a fallen tree had broken the telephone line so the telephone didn't work. Kim began to feel that she was stuck on an island.

What good was a day off if you couldn't have any fun? Because her father saw the unhappy look on Kim's face, he told her that when the snow stopped, they could all go outside and make snow people. Kim's mother told her to find some old clothes to use for dressing the snow people. Now Kim was excited. Maybe this storm would be fun after all.

NAME_____

1. Why hadn't Kim's mother been able to go to the store during the last big storm?

(a) The stores had been closed.

(b) The snow had been too deep.

(c) She had been too tired.

(d) She didn't need anything.

cause/effect

2. Which word from the story helped you choose your answer?

(a) because

(b) when

(c) last

(d) almost

cause/effect

3. Why couldn't Kim go to school?

(a) Her father wouldn't let her.

(b) Her friend was coming over.

(c) All the roads were closed.

(d) A tree had fallen.

cause/effect

4. Which words from the story helped you choose your answer?

(a) had fallen

(b) could call

(c) were closed

(d) as a result

cause/effect

5. What happened because a fallen tree broke the telephone line?

(a) All the roads were closed.

(b) Kim's father couldn't go to work.

(c) The telephone didn't work.

(d) Kim's friend came over.

cause/effect

6. Which word from the story helped you choose your answer?

(a) so

(b) had

(c) the

(d) didn't

cause/effect

7. Why did Kim's father say they could make snow people?

(a) He liked to play.

(b) The snow had stopped.

(c) He saw that Kim was unhappy.

(d) He was stuck on an island.

cause/effect

8. Which word from the story helped you choose your answer?

(a) Because

(b) As a result

(c) Now

(d) outside

127

LITERATURE

Story Elements

> **REMEMBER:** To help you understand stories, look for clues and details that tell about the setting of the story.

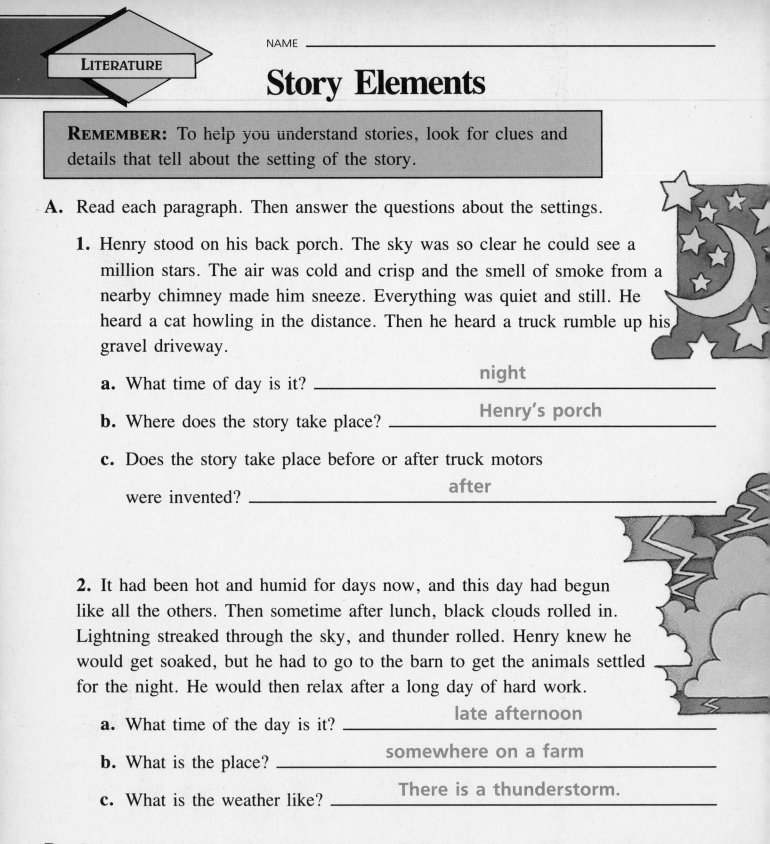

A. Read each paragraph. Then answer the questions about the settings.

1. Henry stood on his back porch. The sky was so clear he could see a million stars. The air was cold and crisp and the smell of smoke from a nearby chimney made him sneeze. Everything was quiet and still. He heard a cat howling in the distance. Then he heard a truck rumble up his gravel driveway.

a. What time of day is it? _____ night _____

b. Where does the story take place? _____ Henry's porch _____

c. Does the story take place before or after truck motors

were invented? _____ after _____

2. It had been hot and humid for days now, and this day had begun like all the others. Then sometime after lunch, black clouds rolled in. Lightning streaked through the sky, and thunder rolled. Henry knew he would get soaked, but he had to go to the barn to get the animals settled for the night. He would then relax after a long day of hard work.

a. What time of the day is it? _____ late afternoon _____

b. What is the place? _____ somewhere on a farm _____

c. What is the weather like? _____ There is a thunderstorm. _____

B. On separate paper, write three sentences. Tell about the setting of a story in your reading book that you liked. See Teacher Notes.

NAME _____

Using New Words

A. Write the word from the box that best fits each meaning.

churned	levees	possum	rescued

1. _____churned_____ moved around with great force

2. _____possum_____ small animal that plays dead when in danger

3. _____levees_____ piles of earth built up near a river to keep
   the water in

4. _____rescued_____ saved from danger

B. Complete each sentence with a story word.

5. The farmers were _____rescued_____ from the roof of the barn.

6. Since the rainstorm made the river rise, people built

   _____levees_____ to keep the water from flooding.

7. The _____possum_____ was so still, it almost looked like it was dead.

8. The water in the river moved so quickly, it _____churned_____ and
   tossed big branches around as if they were toothpicks.

C. On separate paper, write four sentences that tell how you would
rescue a possum from danger. Use at least two story words in
your sentences. **See Teacher Notes.**

NAME _____

Mississippi Possum

A. Complete the summary of the story "Mississippi Possum."
   Accept reasonable variations.

This story is about a little _____**possum**_____ and a girl

named _____**Rose Mary**_____ . It takes place mainly at a campground

near the _____**Mississippi**_____ River during a flood.

The little possum lived in a _____**log**_____ . He was

_____**afraid**_____ of many things, especially people. He
could find nothing to eat since the rains had started. He saw
Jefferson and his sister looking at the river and hid from them.

Jefferson and his sister ran home to tell their parents about

the rising river. Their father said they should _____**move**_____

_____**to higher ground**_____ . As they left, they

passed what looked like a poor, _____**dead possum**_____ .

The possum also had to get away from the flooding river. It was
night when the possum reached the top of the hill. He was tired and
hungry. In the first tent he saw what looked like four logs. When Rose
Mary and her family woke up, the possum pretended he was dead. Rose

Mary put some _____**berries**_____ in front of him to see if he was

just _____**pretending**_____ to be dead. The possum ate the
berries. Then he climbed onto the girl's shoulder.

Finally, the river water went down, and the family went back to
their home. The possum traveled on Rose Mary's

_____**shoulder**_____ . Rose Mary kept the possum, and he lived in
a log near the back door. He wasn't afraid of people any more.

B. On separate paper, write about an adventure Rose Mary and the
   possum might have once he is living near her back door. **See Teacher Notes.**

Cause/Effect

REMEMBER: Use signal words, story clues, and what you already know to figure out which events caused other events to happen.

A. Read the paragraph. Then write answers to the questions about causes and effects.

   The rain had fallen for a long time. The river water rose so high that the levee began to break. People worked to make the levee stronger, but their work was in vain. When the water finally broke through, the land for miles around was flooded. The flood brought many changes. Rabbits and dogs ran from the river together because they were too scared to think about being enemies. As the possum ran, he saw people coming behind him. Since there was no place to hide, he lay down on the ground and did not move.

1. Why did the river rise? The rain had fallen for a long time.

2. What made the levee begin to break? _____
   The river water rose very high.

3. What happened when the water broke through the levee? _____
   The land for miles around was flooded.

4. Why did dogs and rabbits travel together? _____
   They were too scared to be enemies.

5. What did the possum do when it couldn't find a place to hide? _____
   He lay motionless on the ground.

B. Imagine what it would be like to see a flood. On separate paper, write three effects a flooded street would have on your family. See Teacher Notes.

Long Word Decoding

> **REMEMBER:** When you try to read a long word, look for words and word parts you know.

A. Underline the word parts you know that begin and end each word. Then write the word without the word part or parts. Remember that some words change their spelling when word parts are added.

1. reanswering   answer

2. discontinuing   continue

3. recircling   circle

4. disabling   able

5. dishonorable   honor

6. disgraceful   grace

B. Read the sentence. Write the underlined word. Then write any word parts that begin or end the word.

7. The possum is repositioning himself on the log.

     repositioning   re-, -ing

8. Some people during the storm were distrustful of others.

     distrustful   dis-, -ful

9. The people and the animals were amazingly calm.

     amazingly   -ing, -ly

C. On separate paper, write sentences for two words in Part A.
   See Teacher Notes.

Test-Taking

> **REMEMBER:** To do well on a test, prepare well, read directions carefully, and look over the test before beginning.

A. Read the sample directions for taking a test. Then answer the questions about the directions.

DIRECTIONS: Read each unfinished sentence and the answer choices. Choose the answer that best completes each sentence. Draw a circle around the correct answer. Be sure to circle only one answer for each sentence.

1. What do you do before you choose an answer? **You read each unfinished sentence and the answer choices.**

2. How do you mark your answer choice? **You draw a circle around it.**

3. How many answers may you choose for each sentence? **You may choose only one answer for each.**

B. Now practice taking a test. Use the directions you read in Part A.

4. The possum was not afraid of _____.   **a.** mice   **b.** owls

5. The river rose because of the _____.   **a.** ocean   **b.** rain

6. The people's houses were _____.   **a.** flooded   **b.** burned

7. The possum was usually very _____.   **a.** scared   **b.** brave

C. Think of some facts you have learned about possums. On separate paper, make up a practice test with several multiple-choice or true/false questions about possums. Write a set of directions for your test. **See Teacher Notes.**

COMPREHENSION

Predicting Outcomes

> **REMEMBER:** When you **predict,** you make a guess about what will happen in a story. Use story clues and what you know to make a good prediction.

A. Read each story. Then write a prediction about what will happen next. Then write the story clues you used.

1. The possum was far from his log. The possum felt very hungry. Since the rain had begun, he had not found any food. If only he could find the sweet berries he loved. Just then, the possum caught the smell of some berries. It smelled like they were nearby.

Prediction: _The possum will find the berries and eat them._

Story Clues: _He is hungry. He loves berries. He smelled them nearby._

2. The possum searched the grass until he found the berries. The possum ate so many he started to feel sleepy. He needed to find a dry place to sleep. The possum wished for a hollow log. He kept walking. He felt sleepier and sleepier. Just then he saw a hollow log.

Prediction: _He will go into the hollow log to sleep._

Story Clues: _He is sleepy. He needs a dry place._

3. The possum walked until he got to the log. Then he bent down to enter the log and get out of the rain. He couldn't wait to be asleep. Then he saw two eyes inside the log looking out at him. It was a fox! The possum knew that the fox didn't want to share the log with him.

Prediction: _The possum will not go in the log. He will keep looking._

Story Clues: _The fox is in the log. The possum knew the fox didn't want him in the log._

B. Think about clues that predict the weather. On separate paper, make a chart showing the clues and predictions. **See Teacher Notes.**

Using New Words

A. Read each example. Use the underlined words to help you write the correct word from the box in each blank.

herdsmen	migrated	mooed	pasture	slender

1. When one of the farmer's cows <u>made a sound</u>, she knew right away which one had _____**mooed**_____ .

2. Sue needed a _____**slender**_____ stick to use for walking, so she cut a <u>long and thin</u> one from a bush.

3. We saw some <u>people who take care of groups of animals</u> and asked these _____**herdsmen**_____ where the wild buffaloes were.

4. They said the wild animals had <u>moved from one place to another</u> because they always _____**migrated**_____ when it turned cold.

5. Tame animals eat the hay we give them, but wild animals can't <u>feed on the grass</u> here in winter. They need a warmer place to _____**pasture**_____ .

B. Write a word from the box next to its synonym.

6. moved _____**migrated**_____

7. thin _____**slender**_____

C. Imagine that you are visiting a farm. On separate paper, describe what you would see or hear there. Use three words from the box. **See Teacher Notes.**

BRINGING THE RAIN TO KAPITI PLAIN

A. Complete the summary of the story ''Bringing the Rain to Kapiti Plain.'' **Accept reasonable variations.**

This story is about a man named ___**Ki-pat**___ and how he brought the rain. It takes place on the ___**Kapiti Plain**___ in Africa.

One year ___**rain**___ had not fallen on the great plain. All the cows were hungry and mooed for the rain to fall. The grass was brown and ___**dead**___ . The people needed the rain to fall from the black ___**clouds**___ that shadowed the ground on the plain.

Ki-pat stood on one ___**leg**___ like a stork and watched his hungry cows. Then an eagle dropped a ___**feather**___ that fell on the ground near Ki-pat. Ki-pat wondered how to make it rain.

Ki-pat had an idea. He made an arrow using a stick and the feather. Then he made a bow using ___**a leather thong**___
___**and a string**___ .

As he stood on one leg watching his hungry cows who were mooing on the brown grass, he took the arrow and shot it into the sky.

The arrow went up and pierced the ___**clouds**___ and let loose the rain over the plain. This happened all because an eagle
___**dropped a feather that helped to change the weather**___ .

Now Ki-pat has fat cattle, a wife, and a little Ki-pat who watches the cows and who shoots down the rain from the black clouds.

B. On separate paper, write about an adventure Ki-pat and his son could have on the plain now that there is enough rain. **See Teacher Notes.**

Dictionary

> **REMEMBER:** You use a **dictionary** to learn the spelling, pronunciation, meaning, and origin of words.

A. Read each pair of guide words. Then write if each word would be *before, on,* or *after* the page with those guide words.

1. help - here

    a. herd _____on_____

    b. horn _____after_____

    c. hard _____before_____

2. boat - bow

    a. both _____on_____

    b. black _____before_____

    c. box _____after_____

3. plain - please

    a. pin _____before_____

    b. plant _____on_____

    c. plus _____after_____

4. goat - grass

    a. gone _____on_____

    b. gave _____before_____

    c. grow _____after_____

B. Write the words in the box next to the dictionary respelling that shows how to say the word.

drain	drought	pain	plain

5. plān _____plain_____

6. pān _____pain_____

7. drān _____drain_____

8. drout _____drought_____

C. On separate paper, make up a set of guide words for an imaginary dictionary page with your first name on it. **See Teacher Notes.**

Checkpoint

A. Read the dictionary page. Then fill in the circle beside the correct answer.

---

man·age·a·ble (man′ij ə b′l) *adjective*. that can be managed or controlled.

march (märch) *verb*. walk with even steps.

mar·ga·rine (mär′jə rin) *noun*. a food used instead of butter.

mar·ket (mär′kit) *noun*. 1. an outdoor place where many things are sold. 2. a store where food is sold.

marsh (märsh) *noun*. area of low, wet land.

mash (mash) *verb*. crush.

ma·te·ri·al (mə·tir′ē əl) *noun*. the stuff of which a thing is made.

math·e·ma·ti·cian (math′ə mə tish′ən) *noun*. a person who is an expert in math.

---

pronunciation key: a as in **ask**,   ā as in **ape**,   ä as in **car**;   e as in **ten**,   er as in b**erry**,
ē as in **even**;   i as in **is**,   ir as in h**ere**,   i as in **ice**;   o as in h**ot**,   ō as in **open**,
ô as in **law**;   u as in **up**;   ə as in **about**

---

dictionary

1. What does <u>market</u> mean in this sentence?

Shopping outside at the <u>market</u> made her cold.

(a) an outdoor place where many things are sold

(b) a store where food is sold

(c) an area of low, wet land

(d) a food used instead of butter

dictionary

2. The <u>a</u> in <u>mash</u> has the same vowel sound as the <u>a</u> in _____ .

(a) ask

(b) ape

(c) car

(d) about

long word decoding

3. How many syllables are in the word <u>mathematician</u>?

(a) 3

(b) 4

(c) 5

(d) 6

long word decoding

4. Which word completes this sentence?

Jerry found the work _____

(a) material

(b) manageable

(c) market

(d) mathematician

B. Read the paragraph. Then fill in the circle beside the correct answer.

> Most bears do not like the cold winter weather. When it gets cold, bears will usually go inside a cave and sleep. Because they have a lot of fat, they don't need to eat. They sleep for most of the winter. When it begins to get warm, they wake up.

cause/effect

5. Why don't bears need to eat when they go into their caves?

(a) They have a lot of fat.

(b) The winter is too cold to eat.

(c) The cave is too dark.

(d) They only like warm weather.

cause/effect

6. Which word from the story helped you choose your answer?

(a) Because

(b) When

(c) Most

(d) usually

Vocabulary Review

Fill in the circle beside the word that best fits in the sentence.

1. The cows in the pasture _____ on their way back to the barn.
- (a) migrated
- (b) churned
- (c) boasted
- (d) **mooed**

2. Very high winds in the desert can cause _____ sandstorms.
- (a) valuable
- (b) **tremendous**
- (c) slender
- (d) professional

3. That kind of palm tree has a thin, or _____ , trunk.
- (a) **slender**
- (b) tremendous
- (c) extraordinary
- (d) balance

4. The prize for the safety poster _____ is a new bicycle.
- (a) gust
- (b) hurricane
- (c) **contest**
- (d) moisture

5. In order to stay out of the hot sun, the _____ who take care of groups of animals stay near the trees.
- (a) **herdsmen**
- (b) advisers
- (c) orchestra
- (d) levees

6. In bad weather, people who fly airplanes use an instrument that uses _____ to help them know where they are.
- (a) retina
- (b) loops
- (c) **radar**
- (d) levees

7. When cold weather and heavy winds bring storm clouds toward you, the meteorologist may _____ bad weather.
- (a) **forecast**
- (b) bind
- (c) ignore
- (d) bunt

8. The clown who wore the funny shoes _____ that his shoes were also the biggest.

  a) rescued

  b) migrated

  c) boasted

  d) churned

9. Because they were thirsty, the animals _____ to another place that had more water.

  a) mooed

  b) boasted

  c) migrated

  d) churned

10. A small animal that sometimes plays dead when it is in danger is a _____ .

  a) possum

  b) leopard

  c) bicuspid

  d) radar

11. The air that surrounds the earth is called its _____ .

  a) forecast

  b) contest

  c) atmosphere

  d) radar

12. The people built _____ to keep the river from overflowing during storms.

  a) droughts

  b) workshops

  c) arches

  d) levees

13. Opening the door during the heavy winds brought a sudden _____ of air into the room.

  a) pasture

  b) gust

  c) possum

  d) atmosphere

14. A scientist who studies the weather is called a _____ .

  a) forecast

  b) meteorologist

  c) formula

  d) violinist

15. The people who were lost in the snowstorm were _____ this morning.

  a) churned

  b) migrated

  c) mooed

  d) rescued

Unit Wrap-Up

NAME _____

Read each question. Write your answer, using complete sentences.

1. Think about ''An Interview with a Meteorologist.'' What kind of information could a meteorologist like Mr. Dreumont have given the people in ''Mississippi Possum'' that would have helped them deal with the flood? **Possible response: He might have predicted the heavy rains and told the people that the ground was too wet to hold the water. By warning them ahead of time, he could have helped them get ready for the flood.**

2. In ''The Wind and the Sun,'' you read about how the weather caused a person to dress differently. In what other ways do people protect themselves against the weather? **Possible response: People build houses to keep out rain, wind, and cold. They have heat when it is too cold and air conditioning when it is too hot.**

3. In ''Bringing the Rain to Kapiti Plain,'' Ki-pat ended the drought by shooting an arrow. Do you believe such a solution is possible? Why or why not? **Possible response: Students should recognize that Ki-pat's solution is not a scientific possibility.**

ON THE HORIZON

SILVER BURDETT & GINN

Sterling Edition

NAME _____

Title _____

Author _____

Character's Name _____

You Have called up one of your favorite characters from this Book. What will you say?

How Many Stars? Circle your answer.
☆☆☆☆ Super!!
☆☆☆ Very Good
☆☆ O.K.
☆ Not Good

144

NAME _____

BOOK LOG

TITLE

AUTHOR

NAME THREE NEW THINGS YOU HAVE LEARNED BY READING THIS BOOK.

1.

2.

3.

WHAT DO YOU FIND MOST FASCINATING ABOUT THIS BOOK?

NAME THREE THINGS IN THIS BOOK THAT YOU ALREADY KNEW.

1.

2.

3.

How Many Stars?
Circle your answer.
✩✩✩✩ Super!!
✩✩✩ Very Good
✩✩ O.K.
✩ Not Good

NAME _____

Title

Author

Characters

Setting

Problem

How Many Stars?
Circle your answer.
★★★★ Super!!
★★★ Very Good
★★ O.K.
★ Not Good

NAME _____

This is A T.V. COMMERCIAL FOR....

_____
TITLE

by _____
AUTHOR

ANNOUNCER HOLDING UP BOOK
AND SAYING...

YOU'LL LOVE IT WHEN...

THIS BOOK IS...

THE WORD THAT DESCRIBES
THIS BOOK IS...

How Many Stars?
★★★★ Super!!
★★★ very good
★★ O.K.
★ Not good
circle your answer

NAME _____

MAKE A **BOOKMARK** FOR YOUR BOOK

DRAW A **PICTURE** FROM THE BOOK

WRITE A FEW **WORDS** THAT WILL REMIND YOU OF THE BOOK

TITLE _____

AUTHOR _____

How Many Stars?
Circle your answer.
☆☆☆☆ Super!!
☆☆☆ Very Good
☆☆ O.K.
☆ Not Good

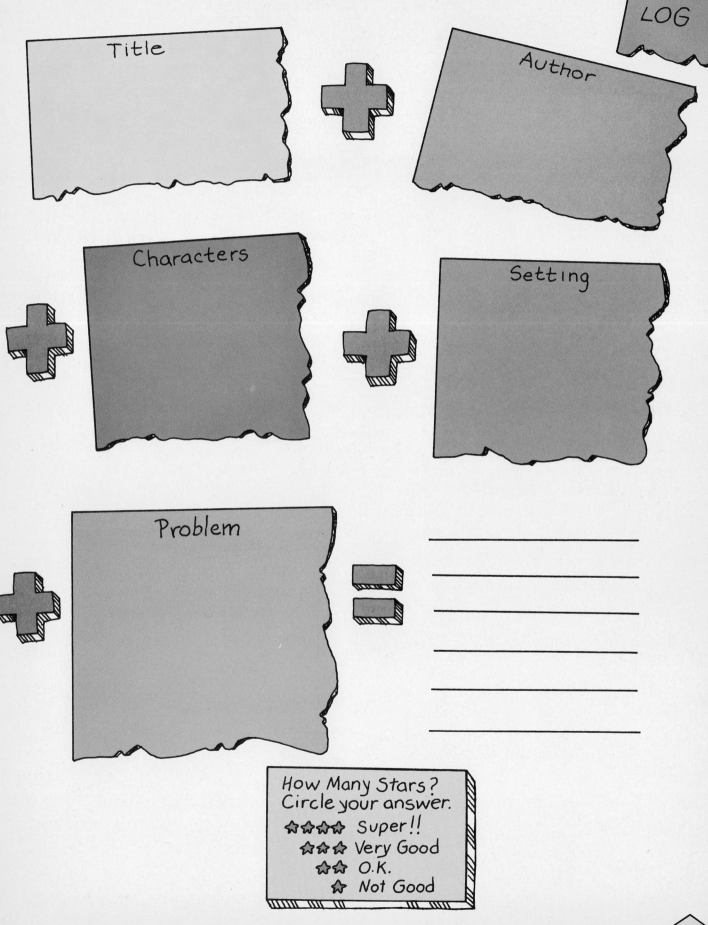

Title

Author

Characters

Setting

Problem

How Many Stars?
Circle your answer.
✰✰✰✰ Super!!
✰✰✰ Very Good
✰✰ O.K.
✰ Not Good

BOOK LOG

TITLE

AUTHOR

NAME THREE NEW THINGS YOU HAVE LEARNED BY READING THIS BOOK.

1.

2.

3.

WHAT DO YOU FIND MOST FASCINATING ABOUT THIS BOOK?

NAME THREE THINGS IN THIS BOOK THAT YOU ALREADY KNEW.

1.

2.

3.

How Many Stars? Circle your answer.
☆☆☆☆ Super!!
☆☆☆ Very Good
☆☆ O.K.
☆ Not Good

Book Log

Title _____

Author _____

Character's Name _____

You Have called up one of Your Favorite characters from this Book. What will You say?

How Many Stars? CIRCLE YOUR ANSWER.

★★★★ Super!!

★★★ very GOOD

★★ O.K.

★ NOT GOOD

NAME _____

BOOK LOG

This is A T.V. COMMERCIAL FOR....

_____
TITLE

by _____ AUTHOR

ANNOUNCER HOLDING UP BOOK AND SAYING...

YOU'll LOVE IT WHEN...

THIS BOOK iS...

THE WORD THAT DESCRIBES THIS BOOK IS...

How Many Stars?
★★★★ Super!!
★★★ Very good
★★ O.K.
★ Not good
circle your Answer

BOOK LOG

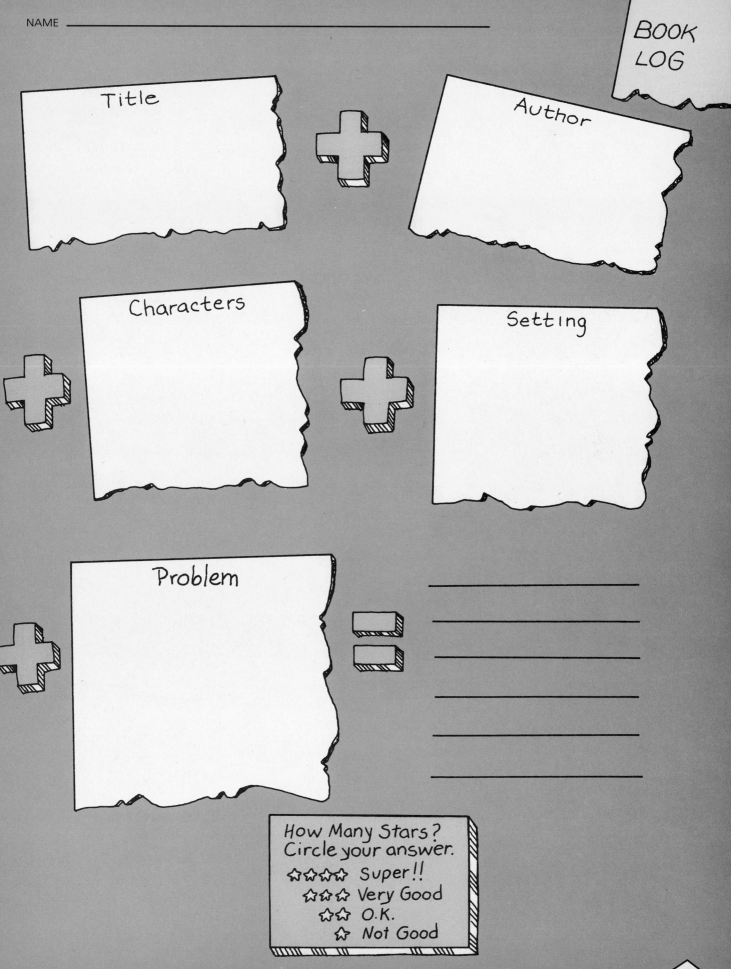

Title

+

Author

Characters

+

Setting

+

Problem

☐
☐

=

_____
_____
_____
_____
_____

_____

How Many Stars?
Circle your answer.
☆☆☆☆ Super!!
☆☆☆ Very Good
☆☆ O.K.
☆ Not Good

MAKE A **BOOKMARK** FOR YOUR BOOK

DRAW A **PICTURE** FROM THE BOOK

WRITE A FEW **WORDS** THAT WILL REMIND YOU OF THE BOOK

TITLE _____

AUTHOR _____

How Many Stars?
Circle your answer.
✰✰✰✰ Super!!
✰✰✰ Very Good
✰✰ O.K.
✰ Not Good

NAME _____

Book Log

Title _____
Author _____

Character's Name
_____

You have called up one of your favorite characters from this book. What will you say?

How Many Stars? Circle your answer.
★★★★ Super!!
★★★ Very Good
★★ O.K.
★ Not Good

PAGE 7   **PART B:**   Answers will vary, but responses should include that a fast boat in rough seas *defies*, or refuses to yield to, bad weather.
    REUSE OPTION: Have students circle the words in the quoted passages that helped them understand the underlined words.

PAGE 8   **PART B:**   Responses will vary. Encourage students to be imaginative and to use describing words in their stories.
    REUSE OPTION: Have students underline the unrealistic details they found in the fantasy sentences.

PAGE 9   **PART C:**   Responses will vary. Encourage students to be inventive. If students create new words, remind them to indicate what words they used.
    REUSE OPTION: Have students read the sentences in Part A again and then underline the clues that show each story word's meaning.

PAGE 10   **PART B:**   Responses will vary. Encourage students to think of their favorite colors and shapes in designing their dream house.

PAGE 11   **PART B:**   Responses will vary. Sentences should reflect the correct meaning and usage of each homograph.
    REUSE OPTION: Have students think of another meaning for the word *present* as it is pronounced in the first example in number 3 of Part A. Have them write in the margin an example sentence for this meaning and write a definition of the word used in this way (a birthday *present;* a gift).

PAGE 12   **PART B:**   Responses will vary. Sentences should be logical and include appropriate context clues.
    REUSE OPTION: Have students reread Part A and underline the clues in each sentence that show the meaning of the underlined word or words.

PAGE 13   **PART C:**   Responses will vary. Students should use synonyms and antonyms other than those in Parts A and B. Responses should indicate an understanding of synonyms and antonyms.
    REUSE OPTION: Have students write in the margin as many more synonyms as they can for *big* and *large.* Then have them write as many antonyms as they can.

PAGE 14   **PART C:**   Responses will vary. Encourage students to be creative. Riddles should be logical and reflect an understanding of vocabulary words.
    REUSE OPTION: Have students use as many story words as they can in one sentence. Have them write it under the boxed words.

PAGE 15   **PART B:**   Responses will vary. Encourage students to think about what they think is beautiful before they answer.

PAGE 16   **PART C:**   Responses will vary. Responses should include antonyms other than those in Part B. Sentences should be logical and reflect an understanding of antonyms.
    REUSE OPTION: Beside each sentence in Part A, have students write an antonym for the underlined word.

PAGE 17   **PART B:**   Responses will vary. Sentences should be logical and include a reasonable comparison.

REUSE OPTION: Have students add another detail describing Alice's grandfather to the bottom of the Alike-and-Different Chart. Then have students complete the chart for that detail.

PAGE 18   **PART C:**   Responses will vary. Encourage students to make a list of their steps and then number them in the correct order. Responses should reflect a logical sequence, aided by the use of signal words.
    REUSE OPTION: Have students read the paragraph in Part B again and find at least three antonym pairs. Have them draw lines connecting each antonym to its opposite.

PAGE 19   **PART C:**   Responses will vary. Stories should be fairly cohesive and should reflect correct use of vocabulary words.
    REUSE OPTION: Have students underline the words in the box which contain recognizable base words. Have them circle each base word.

PAGE 20   **PART B:**   Responses will vary. Responses should be in friendly letter form and should include a formed opinion.

PAGE 21   **PART C:**   Responses will vary. Remind students to use signal words in their steps. Responses should indicate a logical progression.
    REUSE OPTION: Have students circle all the signal words in Parts A and B.

PAGE 24   **PART B:**   Responses will vary. Responses may be reasonable or fanciful. If necessary, help students brainstorm a few silly effects.
    REUSE OPTION: Have students reread the paragraph in Part A and draw an arrow from each cause to its effect.

PAGE 25   **PART C:**   Responses will vary. Suggest to students that they review Part A for ideas. Responses should demonstrate correct use of vocabulary words.
    REUSE OPTION: Have students write the base word beside each of these story words in the box: *assigned, unusual, librarian, calculator.*

PAGE 26   **PART B:**   Responses will vary. Encourage students to be inventive. Responses may be reasonable or fanciful.

PAGE 27   **PART C:**   Responses will vary. Remind students to order entries alphabetically by last name.
    REUSE OPTION: Have students go back to Part A and circle the letter under which each name would be listed in the phone book. Then have them add to the bottom of Part A their own name and the way it would be listed in the white pages.

PAGE 28   **PART C:**   Responses will vary. Responses should include at least three events and should clearly indicate order by use of signal words.
    REUSE OPTION: Have students circle all the signal words in Parts A and B.

PAGE 29   **PART B:**   Responses will vary. Encourage students to think of several details and to choose the ones they liked the best. Paragraphs should contain a main idea supported by details.

REUSE OPTION: Have students number the detail sentences in the paragraphs in Part A in the order in which they actually would have happened.

PAGE 30   PART C: Responses will vary. Sentences should be logical and demonstrate correct use of vocabulary words.

REUSE OPTION: Have students circle the story words that are plural nouns and underline those that are singular nouns. Tell them to try to name the part of speech of the one word that is not a noun.

PAGE 31   PART B: Responses will vary. If necessary, help students brainstorm a few headings: *height, weight, hair/eye color,* and so on. Responses should demonstrate an ability to use comparison.

PAGE 32   PART C: Responses will vary. Remind students that their paragraphs to entertain may be fanciful, while those to inform should be reasonable. Have students reread their paragraphs to check for spelling and punctuation errors.

REUSE OPTION: Have students add one more example to each list in Part B.

PAGE 33   PART B: Responses will vary. Encourage students to think about how their thumbprints and their eyes are different from those of their classmates. Have students use describing words in their sentences.

REUSE OPTION: Find two words in Part A that you think may be hard for some people. Write a sentence for each word that tells the meaning of the word.

PAGE 34   PART B: Responses will vary. Remind students to form a picture in their minds to help them think of activities. Signal words and sequence should be clear and correct.

REUSE OPTION: Have students circle any signal words that helped them decide the sequence of events in the examples in Part A.

PAGE 35   PART B: Responses will vary. Responses should be in standard letter form, and should reflect an understanding of vocabulary words.

REUSE OPTION: Have students label the vocabulary words with the number of syllables each contains.

PAGE 36   PART B: Responses will vary. Have students review the selection before they write their question and answer. Responses should be consistent with what students know about Beverly Cleary.

PAGE 37   PART D: Responses will vary. Responses should use synonyms and antonyms other than those in Parts A, B, and C. Sentences should demonstrate an understanding of synonyms and antonyms.

REUSE OPTION: Have students choose one pair of antonyms from Part C. Have them write synonyms beside each antonym in the pair.

PAGE 45   PART B: Responses will vary. Encourage students to be imaginative. Responses should include a logical comparison.

REUSE OPTION: Have students underline the comparisons in the sentences in the first column that make a reader see things in a new way.

PAGE 46   PART B: Responses will vary. If necessary, have students brainstorm a few examples of stories. Students' story clues should be clear and specific.

REUSE OPTION: Have students circle all the words in the second paragraph of Part A that are clues to the story "The Three Little Pigs."

PAGE 47   PART C: Possible responses:
Hornets for sale!
Great to feed your pet leopard!
Special low price!
Keep them in a calabash!

REUSE OPTION: At the bottom of the page, have students write one long, silly sentence that uses five of the story words.

PAGE 48   PART B: Responses will vary. Encourage students to be inventive. Responses may be fanciful.

PAGE 49   PART C: Responses will vary. Remind students to explain what they would do in a way that would make sense to someone else. Have volunteers share their work with the class.

REUSE OPTION: Have students underline three clue words in Parts A and B that helped them figure out the order of the steps.

PAGE 50   PART B: Responses will vary. Responses should include logical predictions and any story information that helped in making their predictions.

REUSE OPTION: Have students underline the first story clue in each part of the story in Part A that helped them make their predictions.

PAGE 51   PART B: Responses will vary. Responses may include how the object looks, feels, smells, tastes, what it does, where it is located, and so on. Have volunteers read their clues and have the class guess the object.

REUSE OPTION: Have students reread the sentences in Part A and circle the words that describe sounds.

PAGE 52   PART B: Responses will vary. Responses should tell what students would need to do and should demonstrate an understanding of vocabulary words.

REUSE OPTION: Have students find five words in the paragraphs in Part A that they can replace with synonyms. Have them cross out each word and write the synonym above the crossed-out word.

PAGE 53   PART B: Responses will vary. Remind students to recall stories they have enjoyed and what kind of person told the stories.

PAGE 54   PART B: Responses will vary. Maps should be clearly labeled and directions should be logical.

REUSE OPTION: Have students draw a path from the elementary school to the police station on the map in Part A.

PAGE 55   PART B: Responses will vary. Detail should be consistent with the topic and should demonstrate an understanding of the passage.

REUSE OPTION: Have students number the details from 1—4, in the order of their preference for using them to tell the story "A Story, A Story."

TEACHER NOTES

PAGE 58 **PART B:** Responses will vary. Accept reasonable causes; responses should be fairly realistic.
REUSE OPTION: Have students reread the paragraph and underline the causes and circle the effects.
PAGE 59 **PART C:** Responses will vary. Sentences should clearly reflect word meaning. Remind students to use commas and periods where needed.
REUSE OPTION: Have students reread the paragraph in Part A and underline the sentence that states the main idea.
PAGE 60 **PART B:** Responses will vary. Encourage students to be imaginative in their responses. Ask volunteers to share their responses with the class.
PAGE 61 **PART B:** Responses will vary. If necessary, help students brainstorm a few examples and remind them that snow can look different (e.g. fresh snow; old, dirty snow). Comparisons should include *like* or *as*.
REUSE OPTION: Have students draw an arrow to link the words that are being compared in each sentence.
PAGE 62 **PART B:** Responses will vary. Responses should demonstrate a familiarity with dictionaries, encyclopedias, and telephone directories and their uses.
REUSE OPTION: Have students underline the sentence in each paragraph in Part A that states the main idea.
PAGE 63 **PART B:** Responses might include: dark clouds, thunder, strong winds. Accept reasonable variations.
REUSE OPTION: In Part A, have students underline the clues they used to make their predictions.
PAGE 64 **PART C:** Responses will vary. Encourage students to be inventive. Responses should demonstrate correct use of vocabulary words.
REUSE OPTION: Have students circle each vocabulary word in Part A that has more than one syllable and draw a box around all the words that are plural.
PAGE 65 **PART B:** Responses will vary. Tell students they may write about any wish they like, but to remember the lesson King Midas learned.
PAGE 66 **PART B:** Responses will vary. Encourage students to be imaginative. Responses should demonstrate an ability to use figurative language for comparison.
REUSE OPTION: Have students choose three sentences in Part A and replace the figurative language with their own comparisons for the underlined words.
PAGE 67 **PART B:** Responses will vary. Encourage students to picture the route in their minds before they begin. Directions should be clear and logical.
REUSE OPTION: Have students follow directions and add these things to the picture in Part A: (1) a pine tree near the river, (2) a triangle flag on a castle tower, (3) a large mountain in the background.
PAGE 68 **PART B:** Responses will vary. Remind students to use examples from the story to back up their ideas. Responses should be in friendly letter form.
REUSE OPTION: Beside Part A sentences 2 and 3, have students write something that Midas or Marygold might have said.

PAGE 69 **PART B:** Responses will vary. Encourage students to use descriptive words. Pictures should be consistent with the sentences.
REUSE OPTION: Have students circle the vocabulary word in the box that is plural. Then have them use that word in a sentence of their own and write the sentence below the box.
PAGE 70 **PART B:** Responses will vary. If necessary, suggest that students picture themselves in the garden and use all the senses: touch, smell, taste, etc. Encourage students to use vivid describing words in their responses.
PAGE 71 **PART B:** Responses will vary. Accept reasonable variations. Responses should include a logical prediction.
REUSE OPTION: Have students underline all the words in both stories in Part A that they used as clues to predict the outcome.
PAGE 79 **PART B:** Responses will vary. Encourage students to think of many different types of machines. Possible responses might be: *radio, television, dishwasher, steam-roller,* and so on.
REUSE OPTION: Have students add two new pairs of items to the chart in Part A.
PAGE 80 **PART B:** Responses will vary. Responses should include logical conclusions and how each was reached.
REUSE OPTION: Have students draw a line under the clues in each paragraph that helped them reach their conclusions.
PAGE 81 **PART C:** Responses will vary. Accept reasonable possibilities. Responses should indicate an understanding of vocabulary words.
REUSE OPTION: Have students read the paragraph in Part B again. Ask them to draw a line under the sentence that tells the main idea.
PAGE 82 **PART B:** Responses will vary. If necessary, suggest that students picture themselves in the time and setting. Remind students to use descriptive language.
PAGE 83 **PART B:** Responses will vary. Responses should include story clues that helped in drawing conclusions.
REUSE OPTION: Have students underline the story clues that helped them to draw their conclusions in Part A.
PAGE 84 **PART B:** Possible responses:
1. The inside of the car would be very wet.
2. I would get wet if I sat in the car.
REUSE OPTION: Have students circle the words in the paragraph in Part A that signal an effect or a cause.
PAGE 85 **PART C:** Responses will vary. Riddles should be logical and should include a definition of the vocabulary words.
REUSE OPTION: Have students circle each boxed word that names a person or persons.

PAGE 86   PART B: Responses will vary. If necessary, help students brainstorm a few examples of gifts that the governor might need. Encourage students to use all their senses when writing their descriptions.

PAGE 87   PART C: Responses will vary. Remind students to name and label their graphs. Have students tell what information their graphs are showing.

REUSE OPTION: Tell students that a walrus weighs 3,000 stones. Have students add this information to the graph in Part A.

PAGE 88   PART B: Responses will vary. Encourage volunteers to share their new words with the class.

REUSE OPTION: Have students circle the words in the box that name things that are alive.

PAGE 89   PART B: Responses will vary. Encourage students to write as though they were explaining the game or hobby to another person. The paragraph should contain a topic sentence and supporting details.

REUSE OPTION: Have students number the sentences that give details about the main idea in each paragraph in Part A.

PAGE 90   PART C: Responses will vary. Encourage students to explain how they would measure them. Responses should demonstrate correct use of vocabulary words.

REUSE OPTION: Have students say each story word in Part A to themselves and write the number of syllables on the line next to the word.

PAGE 91   PART B: Responses will vary. Encourage students to be inventive, but responses should perform the function of measuring rainfall. Have volunteers share their responses with the class.

PAGE 92   PART B: Responses will vary. Remind students to include the answers to their questions. Students may use any types of questions, such as those in Part A. Directions should be clear and questions should have logical answers.

REUSE OPTION: Have students answer the questions in Parts A and B of the sample test.

PAGE 93   PART B: Responses will vary. Remind students to name and label their graphs. Have students tell what information their graphs are showing.

REUSE OPTION: Have students imagine what the rainfall in Seattle might be in February and May. Have them fill in this information on the graph in Part A.

PAGE 96   PART B: Responses will vary. If necessary, help students by example. Meaning of new words should be clearly indicated through context clues.

REUSE OPTION: Have students underline the clues and signals they used to figure out the meanings of the words in Part A.

PAGE 97   PART C: Possible responses:
1. The bridge was raised to let a big boat pass through.
2. The doctor used a sharp instrument to take out the sliver.

REUSE OPTION: Have students read the story words listed in Part A and write beside each word the number of syllables it has.

PAGE 98   PART B: Responses will vary. Remind students to form a picture in their minds of the situation, and to think about all the possible outcomes.

PAGE 99   PART B: Responses will vary. Students may follow forms in Part A to make their graphs.

REUSE OPTION: Have students write the number represented by each bar in the graphs next to or on top of the bar.

PAGE 100   PART B: Responses will vary. Responses will probably indicate that it is cold. Accept reasonable variations.

REUSE OPTION: Have students underline story clues that helped them draw conclusions in Part A.

PAGE 101   PART C: Responses will vary. Sentences should be logical and demonstrate correct use of vocabulary words.

REUSE OPTION: Have students underline the clues in Part B that helped them know which story word to use.

PAGE 102   PART B: Responses will vary. Remind students to imagine that they cannot hear, and to try to explain what music "sounds" like.

PAGE 103   PART C: Responses will vary. Suggest that students rate the songs they use. Have volunteers share their work with the class.

REUSE OPTION: Beside each answer in Part A, have students write a name for each group of words.

PAGE 104   PART B: Responses will vary. Responses should be logical and reflect an ability to compare and contrast.

REUSE OPTION: Have students add one item to the chart in Part A. Have them symbolize the information with a + or a −.

PAGE 105   PART C: Responses will vary. Remind students that they may choose to be an assistant in any field. Responses should indicate an understanding of vocabulary words.

REUSE OPTION: Have students circle each word in the paragraph in Part A that stands for a person.

PAGE 106   PART B: Responses will vary. Encourage students to be inventive. The patient they choose to write about need not be dangerous.

PAGE 107   PART B: Responses will vary. Responses should be logical.

REUSE OPTION: Have students underline the story clues in Part A that helped them to draw their conclusions.

PAGE 115   PART B: Responses will vary. Encourage students to use descriptive words in their responses.

REUSE OPTION: Have students circle all the words on the page that pertain to the *sea, sailing,* and *stormy weather.*

PAGE 116   PART B: Responses may include: No mail or heating deliveries, no trucks bringing food to stores, no way to get to stores, and so on.

TEACHER NOTES

PAGE 116
REUSE OPTION: Have students read the paragraph again and underline the words or phrases that signal cause-and-effect relationships.

PAGE 117 **PART C:** Responses will vary. Encourage students to use their own experiences. Responses should indicate an understanding of vocabulary words.
REUSE OPTION: Have students read the paragraph in Part B again and draw a line under any sentences that mention causes and effects.

PAGE 118 **PART B:** Responses will vary. Encourage students to be inventive, and to think about things that are strong because they are gentle. Have volunteers share their work with the class.

PAGE 119 **PART C:** Responses should be: *cloud, freeze, frozen, hail, ice, rain, sleet, snow, storm, winter*.
REUSE OPTION: Have students draw a circle around each word in the boxes that has a long vowel sound.

PAGE 120 **PART B:** Responses might include: *sunburn, thirst, becoming sweaty, becoming dizzy*, and so on.
REUSE OPTION: Have students read the paragraph again. Have them underline each cause and circle each effect.

PAGE 121 **PART C:** Responses will vary. Words from Parts A and B should not be used. Sentences should reflect an understanding of words with chosen parts.
REUSE OPTION: Have students underline word parts at the beginning and end of the words they wrote in Part B.

PAGE 122 **PART C:** Responses will vary. Encourage students to be realistic. Responses should reflect an understanding of vocabulary words. Have volunteers share their predictions with the class.
REUSE OPTION: Have students underline the word or words in each sentence in Part B that helped them choose the correct story word.

PAGE 123 **PART B:** Responses will vary. Encourage students to be inventive. Have students title their project and tell how they might go about doing it.

PAGE 124 **PART C:** Responses will vary. Sentences should be meaningful and reflect an understanding of long words used.
REUSE OPTION: Have students circle each prefix and underline each suffix in the words they wrote in Part B.

PAGE 125 **PART C:** Responses will vary. Suggest to students that they list the words alphabetically before putting them on their charts.
REUSE OPTION: Have students think of one other word that would belong on the dictionary pages with the guide words in Part A. Have students add each word next to the appropriate dictionary page.

PAGE 128 **PART B:** Responses will vary. Remind students to include the name of the story. Encourage students to use descriptive words in their responses.
REUSE OPTION: Have students underline the words in each paragraph that told them about place. Have them circle the words that told them about time.

PAGE 129 **PART C:** Responses will vary. Responses should be logical and should reflect correct use of vocabulary words.
REUSE OPTION: Have students write one long sentence that includes all four story words.

PAGE 130 **PART B:** Responses will vary. If necessary, help students brainstorm a few examples. Have volunteers share their episodes with the class.

PAGE 131 **PART B:** Responses will vary. Students may draw on prior experiences if this has happened to them. Responses may be reasonable or fanciful.
REUSE OPTION: Have students underline all the statements in the paragraph in Part A which express a cause-and-effect relationship.

PAGE 132 **PART C:** Responses will vary. Sentences should be meaningful and clearly reflect word meaning.
REUSE OPTION: Have students underline the letters they added to complete the base words in Part A (continue, circle, able). Then have them add a different word part to each base word.

PAGE 133 **PART C:** Responses will vary. Remind students to make their directions clear and to indicate the correct answer for each question. Questions should contain only one correct answer.
REUSE OPTION: Have students number the answer choices in Part B in alphabetical order.

PAGE 134 **PART B:** Charts should include two columns. Left column should be labeled *clues* and right column labeled *predictions*. Possible responses may include:

Clues	Predictions
clearing blue sky	sun
dark clouds/thunder	rain
clouds/cold wind	snow

REUSE OPTION: Have students underline the details that served as clues for their predictions.

PAGE 135 **PART C:** Responses will vary. Encourage students to form a picture in their minds before writing their sentences. Responses should demonstrate correct use of vocabulary words.
REUSE OPTION: Have students circle each verb in the box, and then circle the verbs in the underlined portions of Part A.

PAGE 136 **PART B:** Responses will vary. Remind students to think about how plenty of rain could change Ki-pat's life. Responses may include creating a river, planting new crops, using ice, and so on.

PAGE 137 **PART C:** Responses will vary. Guide words should be correct for students' names.
REUSE OPTION: For each pair of guide words in Part A, have students write another word that would be on the same page.

PAGE 137 **PART C:** Responses will vary. Extend this activity further by having students write guide words for a dictionary page with their last name, too.
REUSE OPTION: For each pair of guide words in Part A, have students write another word that would be on the same page.